Oct 6, 1989

To: Dr. E. Harvey Estes, Jr.

In appreciation for your special remarks at the 1st Bowman Gray PA Day Recognition Ceremony.

Thank you.

The Miracle on Hawthorne Hill

THE MIRACLE ON HAWTHORNE HILL

A History of the Medical Center of
The Bowman Gray School of Medicine of
Wake Forest University and the
North Carolina Baptist Hospital

by

Manson Meads, M.D.
Assisted by
Katherine Davis

Wake Forest University
Winston-Salem, North Carolina
1988

CONTENTS

Preface

An institutional history is not destined for the list of best sellers. It is a labor of love written with the hope that a record of the past will broaden the appreciation of what now is and point up inherent qualities that can usefully serve the future. The academic medical center formed by The Bowman Gray School of Medicine of Wake Forest University and the North Carolina Baptist Hospital was born over 40 years ago, though its roots extend to the beginning of this century. It was established with financial resources and facilities that were far from adequate, but with a sense of mission that withstood crises and controversy and developed into an institution that is widely recognized for programs of excellence in medical education, biomedical research, patient care and community service.

In tracing this history from its beginning to July 1983 an attempt is made to highlight significant changes in national and state health policy, socioeconomic trends and unique local and internal factors which strongly influenced the development of the center. Hopefully, this will convey where possible not only what happened, but why it happened.

Sources of information used in compiling this story include extensive administrative files, early published and unpublished historical accounts of the medical school or hospital, annual reports, minutes of meetings of trustees, boards of the Medical Center and faculty councils, the Annuals of the Baptist State Convention of North Carolina, selected reports of North Carolina legislative commissions and the Board of Higher Education, and newspaper accounts. These have been supplemented by personal notes and recollections.

Many hundreds of people within and outside the institution have helped to build the Medical Center. It is not possible to name them all in this text; therefore, of necessity, selection has been limited primarily to those who worked most closely with the administration in governance and in planning, consensus building and resource development. For those readers who desire in-depth histories of the individual departments of the medical school, narratives prepared by the respective chairmen for the Wake Forest University Sesquicentennial in 1984 are available in the archives of the Carpenter Library.

Several topics that deserve attention are documented separately in the Supplemental section, as they could not be adequately integrated into the general narrative. Included are historical accounts of the Department of Denominational Relations and the School of Pastoral Care of the Baptist Hospital, written by the Revs. Calvin Knight and L.L. McGee, respectively. I am grateful to them for these contributions.

Colleagues who have had a long and intimate association with the Medical Center gave considerable time to a review of the original manuscript. I am grateful to Drs. Eben Alexander, C. Nash Herndon, Lucile W. Hutaff, Robert W. Prichard and Ernest H. Yount, and to Reverend Calvin Knight for this effort and for their constructive comments and encouragement. Valuable editorial assistance was given by Mr. Bill D. Glance and Ms. Janice Lewis. Mr. Stuart Wright provided professional assistance in the design of this book and in arrangements for its publication.

The author wishes to express special appreciation for the assistance of Miss Katherine Davis in the compilation of this history. She came to the medical school in 1942 as secretary to Dr. Herbert M. Vann and then served as assistant to Dean Carpenter (1946–1958) and then to me until my retirement in 1983. Her long association in these positions brought her in close touch with faculty, students, employees and alumni, and gave her an intimate knowledge of institutional records and events pertinent to the evolution of the medical center. Her important contribution to this history came from this background and the many hours she gave to research and verification of information and the critical review of the manuscript from its beginning through its final form.

The publication of this history has been made possible in part by generous gifts from members of the family of Bowman and Gordon Gray.

The Miracle on Hawthorne Hill

CHAPTER I

Roots

A new academic medical center consisting of The Bowman Gray School of Medicine of Wake Forest College, in partnership with the North Carolina Baptist Hospital, was founded on August 3, 1939. On this day three remarkable events occurred. The Bowman Gray Fund, established in 1935 through the will of Bowman Gray, Sr., Chairman of the Board of R.J. Reynolds Tobacco Company, was offered officially to the college to establish a four-year medical school in Winston-Salem. The college trustees accepted the offer; and the trustees of the Baptist Hospital invited the school to use the hospital for teaching, agreed to raise the funds to expand bed capacity and accepted a plan for the organization of the medical center. That this happened has been termed "incredible," "audacious," and "an act of faith." These very descriptive terms were used primarily because the Bowman Gray Fund in August 1939 consisted of 14,000 shares of common stock of the R.J. Reynolds Tobacco Company with a market value of $560,000 and cash or its equivalent of $130,000. Additional earnings of $60,000 were projected by August 1941 when the school was to become operational.[1] A total of approximately $750,000 was to be available to establish a new four-year medical school—a fact known by the college a year earlier. Further, there was an internal understanding between the school and the college that no additional moneys from the general fund would be allocated for operations other than those being received by the two-year school—$22,450 per year.

In contrast, Dr. Wilburt C. Davison reported in his history of Duke University Medical Center[2] that, 15 years earlier, the will of James B. Duke bequeathed $10 million to the Duke Endowment, of which up to $4 million was to be used to construct and equip a medical

1

school, hospital and nurses home. Construction of the first two elements cost $3.9 million; a special appropriation of $227,000 was made by the Endowment for library books; the Rockefeller Foundation granted $300,000 to cover the high cost of the initial years, and a "liberal appropriation" was made annually from the university to balance the budget. For the year 1941–1942, when The Bowman Gray School of Medicine opened, Davison estimated that the net cost of undergraduate medical education at Duke (exclusive of grants and patient fees) was $603,544 for the 262 enrolled students.

That the Bowman Gray–Baptist Hospital Medical Center survived and later prospered has been termed "the Miracle on Hawthorne Hill."[3]

Coy C. Carpenter, the driving force and architect of this new medical center, has chronicled much of the early history of Wake Forest medicine, the move of the medical school to Winston-Salem and the early development of the four-year institution.[4] The following briefly describes the highlights of the period leading up to the founding of the center and adds some unrecorded information related particularly to the Baptist Hospital to give proper perspective to subsequent chapters.

Wake Forest Medical School

In his history of Wake Forest College,[5] George W. Paschal indicates that as early as 1849 an article in the *Biblical Recorder* urged the establishment of "A Medical Department for Wake Forest College to be located in Raleigh, North Carolina." As there were no medical schools in the state at the time, students desiring to become physicians went north for this training. A Wake Forest professor wrote in reply that, if this suggestion was followed, it would divert attention from the struggle to pay college debt and provide endowment. The subject was dropped for a third of a century.

During that time medical education in Europe was rapidly gaining a scientific base as a result of striking advances in chemistry, physiology, microbiology and pathology. However with few exceptions, such as at Johns Hopkins, medical education in the United States failed to assimilate these advances and was in disarray. The rapid growth in population and westward migration had sharply increased the need for physicians which was far beyond the capacity of the few good medical schools. This demand had resulted in "an enormous over-production of uneducated and ill trained medical practitioners . . . in absolute disregard of the public welfare . . . Over-production . . . is due in the main to . . . a very large number of commercial schools, sustained . . . by advertising methods through which a mass of unprepared youth is drawn out of industrial occupations into the study of medicine."[6]

When C.E. Taylor was elected president of Wake Forest College in 1875 he was determined not only to raise educational standards, but also to expand offerings beyond training for the ministry. He quietly established a school of law in 1894 and then set his sights on a school of medicine.

The Wake Forest catalogue in 1886–1887 announced a course of study "Preliminary to the Study of Medicine." It was the first recognition by any college in the state of the need for proper premedical preparation. The curriculum included physics, chemistry, physiology, botany and Latin. If the student had sufficient knowledge of the last two subjects he was advised instead to take English, German or minerology and geology.

The first serious consideration by the college trustees of establishing a medical school occurred in May 1893. President Taylor wisely proposed two years of medical instruction, noting later that the medical degree should be offered only by institutions "which can offer the advantage of great hospitals and extensive clinical opportunities of a large city."[7] The town of Wake Forest at the time had a population of approximately 800. A trustee committee was appointed to consider the proposal.

Although the report of this and subsequent committees was favorable, the board as a whole had difficulty coming to an agreement on the matter due to the severe financial constraints under which the college was operating and the question of securing the proper person to head the medical school. President Taylor forced the issue by making a public announcement that a two-year course in medicine would be inaugurated in the fall of 1902. One month before the opening date the trustees elected Dr. Fred K. Cooke as head of the "Medical Department" and as professor of Anatomy, Bacteriology and Pathology at a salary of $1,000 a year. They further asked Professors William L. Poteat (Biology) and Charles E. Brewer (Chemistry) to assist in the medical courses and appropriated $500 for equipment. Thirteen students registered the first year. Tuition was $37.50 per term with extra fees for laboratories and student health care.

The first dean of the school, Dr. Cooke, was a young surgeon from

Louisburg, North Carolina and had graduated from Tulane Medical School in 1901. His father, Judge C.M. Cooke, was a trustee of the college. Despite his lack of credentials for the deanship, he, like President Taylor, was determined from the beginning that the institution must be of high quality. Their goal for the two-year school was that it should become second to none. The high standards established were recognized after inspection and approval by the American Medical Association and acceptance of the school for membership in the Association of American Medical Colleges in 1904. It is noteworthy that at that time there were a dozen or more medical schools in North Carolina, and all were unapproved except for the two-year school at the University of North Carolina at Chapel Hill that had been established in 1879. Dr. Cooke resigned in 1905 because of a severe peptic ulcer and resumed private practice. He died in 1910 at age 34. Dr. Watson S. Rankin succeeded Cooke as dean. Rankin, a pathologist, was recommended by Dr. William H. Welch of Johns Hopkins and had joined the Wake Forest faculty in 1903 at a salary of $1,250. He had graduated from the University of Maryland in 1901 and, after further work at Hopkins where he was greatly influenced by Welch and William Osler, had begun practice in Jacksonville, North Carolina. Rankin declared that the only basis for the existence of Wake Forest Medical School was to train good doctors. This meant high standards and was reflected again in the *Journal of American Medical Association,* which reported in 1907 that Wake Forest Medical School was one of only eleven schools in the country out of a total of 160 that required two years of college for entrance.

The deplorable state of medical education in the United States was highlighted by the Flexner Report in 1910. The year before, Dr. N.P. Colwell, secretary of the Council on Education of the American Medical Association, visited the school on behalf of the Flexner study, which was financed by the Carnegie Foundation for the Advancement of Teaching. His observations were recorded in the report as follows:[8]

Wake Forest College School of Medicine. A half-school. Organized 1902. An integral part of Wake Forest College.

Entrance Requirement: Two years of college work, actually enforced, but resting upon the irregular secondary school education characteristic of the section.

Attendance: 53

Teaching staff: 6 whole-time instructors take part in the work of the department; two of them devote their entire time to medical instruction. *Resources available for maintenance:* The budget is part of the college budget. Fees amount of $2225.

Laboratory facilities: The laboratories of this little school are, as far as they go, models in their way. Everything about them indicates intelligence and earnestness. The dissecting-room is clean and odorless, the bodies undergoing dissection being cared for in the most approved modern manner. Separate laboratories, properly equipped, are provided for ordinary undergraduate work in bacteriology, pathology, and histology, and the instructor has a private laboratory besides. Chemistry is taught in the well equipped college laboratory; physiology is slight; there is no pharmacology. There is a small museum; animals, charts, and books are provided.

Date of visit: February 1909.

The April 1910 Bulletin of Wake Forest College quotes excerpts of a letter from the president of the Carnegie Foundation:

In connection with the highly commendatory report of the Carnegie Foundation on the equipment of the Department of Medicine, portions of a personal letter received during the summer from the President of the Foundation were read as follows: "The admirable work of Wake Forest College in Medicine has been a cheering thing to us in the wide desert of commercial institutions in that region. *** You have served a very admirable purpose in showing what can be done even in an isolated college with modest means under the right spirit and when once the commercial basis is dropped. I am advising some of the rich New England Colleges which have been supporting medicine on the commercial basis to go south to Wake Forest and get a lesson."[9]

Shortly after the Flexner survey Dr. Rankin resigned to become the first full-time Secretary of the North Carolina Board of Health. His studies on the prevalence of hookworm in North Carolina are the first recorded research from the medical school.[10] These studies led to the eventual eradication of the disease in the southern United States and brought national attention to the institution. Dr. Rankin also served for twenty years as a trustee of Wake Forest College. In 1929 he became director of the Hospital Section of the Duke Endowment and was very supportive of the initial expansion of the North Carolina Baptist Hospital in 1940, which was critical to the success of the fledgling four-year medical school.

Following the departure of Dr. Rankin, Dr. John B. Powers, Jr. was appointed acting dean for 1909-10 and dean during 1910-11. Powers, who was age 28, had received the A.B. and M.S. degrees from Wake Forest and the M.D. from Columbia College of Physicians and Surgeons. He was a newly elected professor of Bacteriology and Pathology at Wake Forest when he was appointed acting dean.

Paschal, in his Wake Forest College history, indicates that a long period of wrangling among the faculty of the medical school began after Rankin resigned and lasted for a period of ten years. Carpenter attributed this dissention to several factors, including a policy established in 1909 allowing the medical faculty to engage in private practice in the small community of Wake Forest. The student infirmary soon became, in reality, a community hospital forcing the trustees to take its management away from the physicians and place it in the hands of a lay administrator. The trustees abolished the deanship in 1911 and the school's faculty members were placed on an equal basis, with each reporting directly to the college president.

The two-year curriculum of the school focused on traditional basic science instruction largely through lectures and laboratory demonstrations. On graduation, students transferred for clinical training to such schools as Jefferson Medical College, Temple University, the University of Pennsylvania, the University of Maryland, Long Island Medical College and the University of Virginia.

This was a period in which reforms in medical education were gaining strong momentum through the efforts of the Association of American Medical Colleges, the Council on Medical Education of the American Medical Association, state licensure boards and the catalytic effect of the Flexner Report. The 160 medical schools in 1907 had dwindled to 100 in 1914, with the closing of many proprietary and other substandard schools.[11] This included the only four-year schools in North Carolina: The North Carolina Medical College in Charlotte and the Leonard Medical School for Negroes in Raleigh. Despite the severe constraints on finances and facilities, Wake Forest Medical School continued its approved status. No doubt this was due to the high standards of admission and graduation established by Drs. Cooke and Rankin and the fact that the school was an integral part of a respected college.

Dr. Thurman D. Kitchin and Dr. Coy C. Carpenter emerged as key leaders during the ensuing decade. These two were largely responsible for the survival of the medical school in the 1930s and the establishment of the four-year Bowman Gray School of Medicine in 1941.

In 1919 the deanship was reestablished with the election of Dr. Kitchin to that position. A graduate of Wake Forest College, Kitchin received the M.D. degree from Jefferson Medical College in 1908. After serving as a general practitioner in eastern North Carolina for nine years, he joined the medical school faculty in 1917 as professor of physiology and pharmacology. In 1930 Dr. Kitchin was elected president of the college and carried the dual administrative title until 1936 when Dr. Carpenter became dean.

Dr. Carpenter was also a distinguished product of North Carolina and Wake Forest. He entered Wake Forest College in 1919, graduated from the two-year school of medicine in 1922, and received the M.D. degree from Syracuse University School of Medicine two years later. The following year he was appointed assistant to the dean at Syracuse and instructor in pathology under Dr. Herman Weiskotten. At the urging of Dr. Weiskotten, Carpenter accepted a position as professor of Pathology and Physical Diagnosis at Wake Forest in 1926, as he "thought it might be a good opportunity to make a contribution to the advancement of medicine." This decision and the close relationship and admiration Dr. Carpenter held for Dr. Kitchin were indeed fortuitous in the light of subsequent history.

Clinical teaching had been developed at Rex and St. Agnes Hospitals in Raleigh, 17 miles from the Wake Forest campus. These institutions were used for teaching autopsy pathology, laboratory and physical diagnosis, general medicine and minor surgery. Four distinguished physicians practicing in the community assisted in this instruction.

Following World War I, William Preston Few, President of Trinity College, proposed a cooperative plan to establish a four-year medical school in North Carolina. Trinity would establish a two-year program and, by combining the resources of Watts Hospital and the University of North Carolina, they would together develop the clinical years of medical instruction in Durham. Wake Forest and Davidson Colleges were invited to participate. The plan failed as the University of North Carolina trustees favored a school exclusively controlled by the university and also because the Baptists of North Carolina were against institutional union of church and state. The failure of the cooperative plan and the death of James B. Duke in October 1925 led to the establishment of Duke University and its four-year School of Medicine.[12] However, the controversy surrounding the issue delayed the development of a four-year school at Chapel Hill for more than two decades as the small town, like Wake Forest, lacked adequate facilities for clinical instruction.

The medical school at Wake Forest was moved in 1933 from its limited quarters in the Alumni Building to a new and larger campus facility financed by a memorial gift of $100,000 from the family of William Amos Johnson. Johnson was a young instructor in anatomy who had served on the faculty for one year before his death in an automobile accident on Thanksgiving Day 1927.

The worldwide depression began in November 1929 and its economic impact did not spare the medical profession. Many doctors were forced to seek other employment, some even as taxi drivers or elevator operators. Between 1932 and 1935, widespread opinion built rapidly that too many physicians were being produced. In 1933, Dr. William D. Cutter, secretary of the Council on Medical Education of the American Medical Association, spoke to the annual meeting of the Association of American Medical Colleges and told the deans it was their responsibility to eliminate the excess production of physicians. The following year the Council on Medical Education and the Association of American Medical Colleges instituted a resurvey of all medical schools. Wake Forest was surveyed by Dr. Herman Weiskotten during April 15–17, 1935. He reported to Drs. Kitchin and Carpenter that, because of deficiencies in faculty, facilities and library, the school would have to close. He added that medical education in the state should be left to Duke because it had unlimited funds that would constantly increase; and Wake Forest and the University of North Carolina should abandon the field. Dr. Kitchin reported later that Dean Davison at Duke told him he did not want the total responsibility for medical education recommended by Weiskotten and could not do the job of the two other schools. In September 1935 the Council on Medical Education and Hospitals of the American Medical Association declared that after 1937 it would not recognize any two-year school. There were ten such schools at the time. It then became obvious that this was the council's way of decreasing the production of physicians—close the smaller schools, as they would not be able to defend themselves.

North Carolina is credited with upsetting these plans. On October 2, 1935 the Raleigh *News and Observer* published a statement by Dr. Kitchin, entitled "Fewer Doctors?" in which he documented the history and motivation of the council's edict. The article was circulated to the deans of all medical schools. Dr. W. Reece Berryhill reports that President Frank P. Graham of the University of North Carolina effectively presented the case for the continued approval of the two-year schools to the Association of American Universities and enlisted that organization's support.[13] Dr. Carpenter, in a personal communication, indicated that Dr. Wilburt C. Davison of Duke entertained some powerful deans at the meeting of the Association of American Medical Colleges and helped turn the tide with the aid of "mountain tonic imported from North Carolina." As a result, the association voted unanimously to protest the action of the Council on Medical Education and requested that it rescind its action on two-year schools. One month later the council agreed that two-year schools would continue to be approved and listed officially as "Schools of Basic Medical Sciences." Wake Forest was placed on probation, however, and given until June 1939 to correct deficiencies. Both Dr. Carpenter and Dr. Berryhill reflected that, though the immediate battle was won, the war was not over and the problems of the two-year schools would persist. They recognized that historically two-year schools were insecure because of difficulty in attracting and maintaining able faculty and because of their dependence on four-year schools to accept their students for clinical training. These circumstances and the time served as strong motivation to seek ways to expand "half schools" to four-year institutions. As a result of the action of the Council on Medical Education the name of the school was changed to Wake Forest School of Medical Sciences in 1937.

Dr. Fred Zapffe, secretary of the Association of American Medical Colleges, visited the medical school in 1937 and advised that, if it were to remain classified as an A-1 institution, it must add a full-time faculty member in physiology and pharmacology and in anatomy. The annual expenditure for the school at that time was $38,000. In June 1938 a letter to the dean from Dr. William D. Cutter, secretary of the Council on Medical Education and Hospitals, indicated continued concern for the Wake Forest school and stated, ". . . with no chance of the organization of a four-year medical course we ask your serious consideration of your future." Adding to this pressure, the North Carolina General Assembly authorized Governor Clyde R. Hoey to appoint a commission to study the need for a four-year state medical school and make recommendations prior to the 1939 session of the legislature. This commission, known as the Hoey Commission, had seven members including Dr. Carpenter, Dr. W.M.

MacNider, dean of the University of North Carolina two-year medical school; and Mr. Odus M. Mull of Shelby, North Carolina. Dr. Benjamin J. Lawrence, a surgeon from Raleigh and secretary of the State Board of Medical Examiners, served as Secretary. Mr. Joe Garrett, a state legislator from Rockingham County, was also appointed to serve on the commission, as well as Dr. T.W.M. Long, senator from Halifax; Dr. W.M. Coppridge; and former Supreme Court Judge L.R. Varser of Lumberton. Mr. Mull was named to the commission when Judge Varser was unable to serve, according to the recollections of Dr. Lawrence. Mr. Mull was a highly respected lawyer and Baptist layman, and a close associate of Governor Hoey. Dr. Carpenter has recorded in detail this critical point in history. Briefly, in the fall of 1938, Mr. Mull announced at a meeting of the commission that a "large charitable fund" was available to assist in establishing a four-year medical school provided that it be located in the home city of the donor. According to Dr. Carpenter, Dr. MacNider vigorously objected to the consideration of any location for the school other than Chapel Hill. After the meeting Dr. Carpenter asked Mr. Mull to assist in getting the fund for Wake Forest Medical School, and Mr. Mull replied that he could do this only after the commission's report had been sent to the governor. Debate ensued as to whether or not it was important that a state school be located on a university campus. Dr. MacNider's position prevailed and the final report recommended that the state establish as soon as practical a four-year, degree-granting medical school by adding to the existing facility in Chapel Hill and building an associated 300-bed hospital. The cost of operating a four-year medical school with 50 students in each class was estimated to be $600,000. Mr. Mull had recommended an amendment to eliminate any mention of the location of the school, but his proposal failed.

Dr. Berryhill records in his history that in later conversations with President Frank P. Graham he learned that there was no exploration of the information presented by Mr. Mull by any official university representatives. In general, however, he states that Dr. Graham thought that separating the medical school from the university geographically was of questionable educational soundness. Graham lamented the fact that the Mull amendment had failed and that a definite proposal had not been made directly to the president of the University and Trustees so that it could be explored to its fullest with the representatives of the donor. The donor's representatives were later revealed to be members of the Bowman Gray family of Winston-

Salem, who had close ties with the University of North Carolina. The 1939 legislature did not act on the recommendation of the commission, and it was not until 1947 that appropriations were approved for hospital construction and expansion of the University of North Carolina School of Medicine to a four-year school in Chapel Hill.

It is of interest at this point that Gordon Gray reported many years later that the will of his father did not stipulate that the fund was to be used to establish a medical school in Winston-Salem. It stated only that the fund should be used for the establishment of a charitable project and the beneficiary was to be chosen by a committee consisting of his wife, two sons and brother. Gordon Gray added, however, that his father was intensely community minded and always hoped there would be a medical school in this city to improve the quality of life for all citizens and the well-being of thousands of employees of the Reynolds Tobacco Company. As such, he stated that the decision of the committee was an easy one.[14] One might wonder if the example set by a competitor, James B. Duke in Durham, might have been a factor in Mr. Bowman Gray's desire for a medical school in Winston-Salem.

On November 4, 1938, the day following the formal meeting of the Hoey Commission, Dr. Carpenter met with Mr. Mull and Governor Hoey in Shelby. Mull agreed to serve as chairman of the committee on medical education to be appointed by the Wake Forest trustees and arrange a meeting with the representatives of the Bowman Gray Fund. Dr. Carpenter was advised to go to Winston-Salem and quietly explore with leaders associated with the North Carolina Baptist Hospital their cooperation in moving the medical school to that city. Carpenter reported that he met with Egbert L. Davis, Sr., chairman of the Hospital Trustees; and Dr. Wingate M. Johnson, a highly respected internist and chairman of the Board of Trustees of Wake Forest College. He found great enthusiasm for the proposal.

This was not the first time that the idea of moving the medical school to Winston-Salem in association with the Baptist Hospital had been considered. An article in the Raleigh *News and Observer* November 14, 1929, quoted E.L. Davis, Sr., then president of the Wake Forest Alumni Association and trustee chairman of Baptist Hospital, as indicating that alumni and interested citizens of Winston-Salem had been discussing a move of the medical school to that city to join with Baptist Hospital, and that the idea was gaining favor rapidly. Wake

Forest President Francis P. Gaines and Dean Thurman D. Kitchin reportedly had no comments on the suggestion. The Great Depression occurred shortly thereafter and nothing came of the matter. In addition, a letter from Dr. Kitchin to Mr. Mull dated November 3, 1938 indicated that he and Dr. Carpenter had visited Winston-Salem in 1936 with the secretary of the Association of American Medical Colleges to inspect the Baptist and City Hospitals. The secretary said that he could support two clinical years here, provided these hospitals were utilized for teaching and if an additional $100,000 per year were added to the operational budget of the medical school.

The meeting with Mr. James Gray, spokesman for the advisors of the Bowman Gray Fund, took place on August 2, 1938. Drs. Kitchin and Carpenter and Mr. Mull accepted the fund for Wake Forest if offered, despite their disappointment on learning the amount of money was far less than expected. After a year's delay the fund was officially offered to Wake Forest on August 3, 1939.

Some years later Dr. Benjamin Lawrence wrote an undated and unpublished paper entitled "My Recollections of Some Events Leading to the Establishment of the Bowman Gray Medical School of Wake Forest College." In summary he stated "history should record for posterity, the full knowledge that to Mr. O.M. Mull—stronghearted, wise and courageous statesman and scholar—should go the full measure of credit for persuading the Gray family to donate the funds for establishing the Bowman Gray Medical School. Because it was Mr. Mull, almost single handed, whose influence and leadership accrued this generous donation from that great family of North Carolinians who were willing to give their money in order to establish a great and much needed medical center . . . undoubtedly the most outstanding and greatest accomplishment of Wake Forest College and its friends and the trustees of the College during the presidency of Dr. Kitchin."

North Carolina Baptist Hospital

Background on the origin and early development of the North Carolina Baptist Hospital seems appropriate at this time,[15] as history from 1939 onward involves the hospital and medical school together in the formation and development of an academic medical center.

During the early part of the twentieth century, Southern Baptists, like other denominations, established hospitals in a number of southern states as missionary enterprises directed primarily at the care of the poor. First mention of Baptist interest in establishing a charity hospital in North Carolina appears in an article by Dr. Louis M. Gaines in the *Biblical Recorder* in 1907. Dr. Gaines was professor of Anatomy and Physiology and superintendent of the student hospital at Wake Forest College. With trustee approval he proposed that three charity beds be established for needy patients other than students and that an endowment be sought to maintain these beds. He indicated the cost would be $1.75 per day, and that physicians and surgeons would remit fees. He solicited donations for the endowment but resigned a year after, and apparently nothing came of this idea.

The first serious planning for a Baptist Hospital in North Carolina developed during the Baptist State Convention in Raleigh in 1919. The convention approved the expansion of their Christian Mission to include healing, particularly for the needy, and proposed that $100,000 be set aside from its contributions to the "Seventy-five Million" Southern Baptist campaign to help build a hospital in North Carolina. Applications for the location of the hospital were received from Raleigh, High Point, Charlotte, Greensboro, Salisbury and Winston-Salem.

A hospital commission was appointed in 1920 to select the location. It was stipulated that the local community chosen must provide a suitable site and raise $100,000 toward the construction of the facility. A delegation from the Winston-Salem Chamber of Commerce appeared before the commission, presented a strong case for that rapidly growing community and the needs of the adjacent region, and pledged to meet the requirements. To the chagrin of Gerald Johnson, editor of the *Greensboro Daily News*, and the delight of his first cousin, Dr. Wingate M. Johnson of Winston-Salem, who later played a major role in early medical center history, the commission chose Winston-Salem. The hospital was to be built on 11.2 acres of heavily wooded land on Ardmore Hill. It was reported that the area was known as the "wilds of Ardmore," that only two houses were in the vicinity and that bus service was irregular. The Hospital Commission approved plans for a five-story fireproof facility with 88 beds and 20 bassinets. It was to be constructed by J.A. Jones Construction Company of Charlotte for an estimated cost of $186,000.

With the help of the Baptist Men's Union, $140,000 was raised in a one-day campaign in Winston-Salem in October 1921, with pledges to be paid over 18 months. An additional $25,000 was available through the Baptist State Convention. The Ardmore site was purchased for

$32,000 and construction began in November of that year.

In April 1922, the hospital commission made two important appointments. The Reverend George T. Lumpkin, a pastor of a Suffolk, Virginia Baptist church, was appointed superintendent of the hospital. He was "nearly age 50," and was known as a "builder of churches," including Brown Memorial in Winston-Salem. Miss Edna L. Heinzerling, a native of Salisbury, was appointed director of nursing, formerly having been assistant director of nursing at City Memorial Hospital in Winston-Salem. Shortly thereafter Miss Olivia Hall, also of Suffolk, Virginia, accepted the position as accountant and business manager. They were given temporary office space in the B.F. Huntley Furniture Company until hospital construction was completed.

In December a 12-member board of trustees was named to replace the hospital commission, and Egbert L. Davis, Sr. was elected the first chairman. Mr. Davis, then general sales manager for R.J. Reynolds Tobacco Company, a prominent civic leader and an active Baptist layman, served as chairman of the hospital board through 1940.

The hospital charter, also issued in December 1922, stated that the objects of the institution shall be "to construct, own, maintain, and operate hospitals, sanitoriums, infirmaries, nurses homes and training schools for nurses." The new hospital was dedicated on May 28, 1923 and admitted its first patient two days later. The final cost of construction was $192,628 and was paid for through the limited funds from the convention and a bond issue backed by local campaign pledges and anticipated income. Nothing was available for furnishings, however, so Mrs. J.J. Roddick, a Winston-Salem member of the hospital board, personally raised "between $15,000 and $25,000" from Baptist Associations and other organizations for this purpose. Miss Heinzerling mobilized the women of Baptist churches in the community and later the entire state, to make linens, curtains and bed gowns for the hospital, as there was no money available for these critical items. This work was first done in a room of the Zinzendorf Hotel and these volunteers soon formed a hospital auxiliary with Mrs. Annie Pearl Shore Davis, wife of the chairman of the hospital board, serving as first president.

At the outset, two floors were opened to patients. Local physicians served on the professional staff and services included general surgery, medicine, pediatrics, orthopedics, obstetrics and diagnostic x-ray. Hospital rates were $2.50 a day for ward beds, $3.50 for a semiprivate room, and $4.00 for a private room for those able to pay. David Hailey was the first and only intern and served all departments of the hospital.

The hospital School of Nursing was opened in the summer of 1923 with 15 students. Living quarters were made available on the fifth floor of the hospital next to a suite of operating rooms. Two years later the students were moved to a stucco duplex house across the street as demand for hospital beds increased. By 1927, the number of students had increased to the point that a new nurses home was necessary. Again, Mrs. Roddick rose to the occasion and raised funds throughout the state to meet the $25,000 construction costs and the additional moneys for furnishings. The three-story building located at the corner of Hawthorne Road and Queen Street was occupied in May 1928 and students were taught in basement classrooms by the first full-time instructor, Miss Hettie Reinhart, assisted by staff nurses and physicians.

During its early days, hospital census was low and there was great debate within the convention led by those who felt the purpose of the hospital was primarily to serve the poor. Superintendent Lumpkin asserted that the success of a church hospital depended on the faith and confidence of the adherents of the denomination because no fixed source of income was available. Through personal persuasion and support of the members of the hospital board, the Baptist Convention in 1924 approved the establishment of an annual Mother's Day offering in all associated churches with the proceeds going to the hospital for charity patient care. Eleven thousand dollars was collected in the first year. In addition, the convention agreed that four percent of its annual budget would be allocated for the support of the hospital.

With the onset of the Great Depression in 1929, the hospital faced a major financial crisis. Hospital census dropped to 25 to 30 patients, accounts were difficult to collect, and many who had pledged toward room memorials in the early '20s were forced to default. At that time Egbert L. Davis, Sr. was instrumental in refinancing the hospital debt. The salaries of all personnel were decreased and, according to Miss Heinzerling, were "not changed for a long time." Fortunately, the Duke Endowment initiated a program which contributed $1.00 per day for each charity patient in hospitals in North and South Carolina. Later Mr. Davis mused "when we needed money for payrolls or supplies we went out and got it. I don't recall ever failing." In 1931, Mr. Davis personally contributed funds to purchase radium. Mr. Lumpkin had stated in an earlier report to the convention that this was a major need and the hospital was "humiliated on the occasions when patients had to be sent home without treatment or transferred to the City

15

Hospital" for radium therapy.

During these early days, the description of the duties of Miss Olivia Hall demonstrates the austerity under which the hospital operated. She made all the room reservations, collected bills, admitted patients, filed patient charts, kept financial records, did the payroll, escorted patients to their rooms, and served as secretary to the superintendent. This remarkable woman, known as "thrifty, careful and accurate," finally retired in 1968. At her death in 1977 at age 89, she left her entire estate of $321,650 and her home on Queen Street to the hospital. There is no question that the hospital survived during this early phase because of the dedication, faith and unselfish contributions of Chairman Davis, Reverend Lumpkin, Miss Hall, Miss Heinzerling, and Mrs. Roddick, and the many church volunteers who gave so willingly to the ministry of the institution.

Reverend Lumpkin died suddenly in 1934, and Mr. Smith Hagaman, superintendent of the Watauga County School System, was appointed to take his place. The hospital had recovered from the depression, and was crowded with patients. Beds were placed in halls and the solarium, and waiting lists for patient admissions were long. This condition continued and stimulated discussions of enlarging the facility. This situation coincided with the opportunity offered the medical school to move to Winston-Salem.

References and Notes

1. Letter to Dr. Thurman D. Kitchin from the Committee for the Bowman Gray Fund, August 3, 1939. Wake Forest Trustee Minute Book # 4, page 345 (see photograph).
2. Davison, W.C. The Duke University Medical Center (1892–1960) Reminiscences of W.C. Davison, 1966, p. 18.
   Davison, W.C. The First Twenty Years: A History of Duke University School of Medicine, Nursing and Health Services and Duke Hospital 1930–1950. Bulletin of Duke University 24 (7-A) May 1952, p. 2.
3. Davis, Chester. A Miracle on Hawthorne Hill, feature story, Winston-Salem Journal and Sentinel, August 6, 1972.
4. Carpenter, Coy C. The Story of Medicine at Wake Forest University. University of North Carolina Press, Chapel Hill, 1970.
5. Paschal, George W. History of Wake Forest College, Volume III, Chapter XX, The School of Medicine of Wake Forest College.

Edwards and Broughton Company, Raleigh, North Carolina, 1943.

6. Flexner, Abraham. Medical Education in the United States and Canada. Carnegie Foundation for the Advancement of Teaching, Bulletin No. Four, 1910, Introduction by Henry S. Pritchett, page x.

7. Annual Report of Wake Forest College Trustees 1902

8. Flexner, Abraham. Medical Education in the United States and Canada. Carnegie Foundation for the Advancement of Teaching, Bulletin No. Four, 1910, Page 280.

9. Bulletin of Wake Forest College, 1909–1910, Vol. 5, April 1910.

10. Nicholson, J.L., and Rankin, W. S. Uncinariasis as Seen in North Carolina. Its frequency, etiology, pathological significance, symptoms and treatment. Med. News, N.Y. IXXXV, 978-987, 1904.

11. King, Lester S. The Flexner Report. JAMA 251: 1079–1086 (February 24) 1984.

12. Gifford, James F., Jr. The Evolution of a Medical Center: A History of Medicine at Duke University to 1941. Duke University Press, Durham, North Carolina, 1972

13. Berryhill, W. Reece, Blythe, William B., and Manning, Isaac H. Medical Education at Chapel Hill: The First Hundred Years. Kingsport Press, Kingsport, TN, 1979.

14. Gray, Gordon. The Medical Center—Forty Years of Faith. Address on the 40th Anniversary of the Medical Center. September 14, 1981.

15. Information from the historical files of the Rev. Calvin Knight, unpublished reminiscences of Edna Heinzerling, R.N., and Annuals of the Baptist State Convention of North Carolina.

CHAPTER II

Initial Center Organization and Resources

Public announcement of the Bowman Gray gift and the plan to establish a four-year medical school in Winston-Salem in association with the North Carolina Baptist Hospital was made on August 4, 1939, the day after the agreement was finalized by the three parties concerned. The medical education community was informed through a news note in the *Journal of the Association of American Medical Colleges* in September of that year.[1] The article indicated that an administration and laboratory facility would be built on the property of the North Carolina Baptist Hospital and that the Bowman Gray Fund was "adequate for building and endowment purposes."

With the move of the school settled, detailed planning was initiated. The size of the medical student enrollment was established at 50 students per class. President Kitchin visited several foundations and was unsuccessful in attempts to raise additional financial support. He was advised by Dr. Alan Gregg of the Rockefeller Foundation to use the Bowman Gray Fund to strengthen premedical education at Wake Forest, which of course was not possible under the agreement. Despite severe criticism of the plan by leaders in medical education, with the exception of Dr. Fred C. Zapffe, then secretary of the Association of American Medical Colleges, Dr. Carpenter stated "the one word that explains our action is 'faith.'" Another word could be added—optimism—a characteristic of the dean. A story told by Dr. Felda Hightower illustrates this trait. Hightower, who later became a highly regarded member of the Department of Surgery, was a part-time instructor in Anatomy at the time the move of the school was announced. He asked the dean, "How much money do we really have to develop a four-year medical school?" The dean replied, "Unlimited."

Clinical Facilities

Shortly after the move of the medical school was announced, the Baptist Hospital initiated an enlargement campaign with a goal of $200,000.[2] The purpose was to relieve overcrowding and enable the hospital to cooperate with the school in training physicians. The existing facility was rated as 88 beds and 16 bassinets, but in fact there were 120 beds in use including those crowded in the hallways, alcoves and waiting rooms. The expansion program was to include the addition of 116 beds, an emergency room, operating and delivery rooms and a new heating plant to serve the hospital and medical school. An area for a separate children's department was designated "so they will no longer have to share rooms with grown-ups."

The enlargement program was endorsed by the North Carolina Baptist State Convention through a resolution that commended the trustees and encouraged their efforts to raise the necessary funds. It stated however that this must be done "without in any way involving the denomination or the North Carolina Baptist State Convention in any further debt." It is noteworthy here to point out that the denomination was supporting hospital operations annually through 4% of its Cooperative Program (ranging from $4,853 to $12,456) and the Mother's Day offering (ranging from $13,577 to $24,307). The campaign brochure stated that through prudent management and the assistance of friends, bills had been paid every year since 1930.

Initially it was planned that all hospitals in the county would be used by the medical school to assure adequate clinical teaching facilities for students. These included the City Hospital System (City Memorial, 225 beds; Kate B. Reynolds for negroes, 190 beds; and their associated clinics), Forsyth County Hospital (50 acute and 100 chronic beds); the Junior League Hospital for Indigents (30 nursing-home type beds); and the Methodist Children's Home and Infirmary that served 500 children. A satisfactory agreement with the City Hospital System was negotiated, which included the statement that any expense or cost incurred from using any part of the system for teaching would be paid for by the medical school. Just before the agreement was presented to the Board of Aldermen for approval, Dr. J.B. Whittington, superintendent of the City Hospital, added a qualifying paragraph which stated that the added costs due to teaching would be those over and above the average cost per day per patient, which was to be calculated as the average for the last five years. The record

Original Two-year Medical School, Old Campus, Wake Forest, N.C.

Watson S. Rankin, M.D.   Thurman D. Kitchin, M.D.

Original North Carolina Baptist Hospital (1923)
Winston-Salem

Egbert L. Davis, Sr.

Edna L. Heinzerling, R.N.

Bowman Gray, Sr.

August 3, 1939.

Dr. Thurman D. Kitchin, President,
Wake Forest College,
Wake Forest, North Carolina.

Dear Doctor Kitchin:

We understand that Wake Forest College is interested in expanding its Medical School from a 2-year to a 4-year School and desires to have such 4-year department located in a city where sufficient hospital facilities and clinical material are available, and in answer to your inquiry as to the possibility of resources of the Bowman Gray Fund in the Winston-Salem Foundation being made available for your College in such a development, provided the 4-year Medical School is established in Winston-Salem, and assuming that Wake Forest College can arrange to use as its College hospital the facilities of the North Carolina Baptist Hospital located in Winston-Salem, we advise as follows:

With the understanding that the Medical School will be conducted as an integral part of Wake Forest College, and with the further understanding that all funds that may be received from the Bowman Gray Fund in the Winston-Salem Foundation will be used exclusively for purposes of buildings and operations of the School of Medicine in Winston-Salem, the undersigned, authorized under the will of the late Bowman Gray to designate the use of the above mentioned funds, will direct Wachovia Bank and Trust Company as Trustee of the Winston-Salem Foundation to turn over all of the resources of said Bowman Gray Fund to Wake Forest College for the purposes above enumerated.

For your information, at present there are held in the Fund 14,000 shares of R. J. Reynolds Tobacco Company New Class B Common Stock with current market value of approximately $560,000.00 and in addition cash or its equivalent in the approximate amount of $130,000.00. It is our information that it will be two years before you would begin the operation of the Medical School in Winston-Salem, by which time the cash or equivalent is estimated to be increased through income from the stock by, say, $60,000.00. Cash or equivalent as of August 1941 is estimated, therefore, to be in the amount of approximately $190,000.00, which would make a total in the Fund of about $750,000.00.

Very truly yours,

Letter offering the Bowman Gray Fund to
Wake Forest College to establish a four-year medical school
in Winston-Salem

showed a steady increase in costs during this period, and Dr. Whittington refused to present the agreement to the aldermen without this statement. Negotiations were discontinued, and Dr. Carpenter indicated that the wisdom of this decision was borne out in that, if such a condition had been agreed to, it would have cost the school "the almost unbelievable sum of $300,000 per year" over the ensuing five years.

As a result of the loss of teaching facilities of the City Hospital System, Dr. Carpenter urged further enlargement of Baptist Hospital. An additional wing was added to the expansion program, bringing the total bed capacity to 270 plus 50 bassinets. The total cost of the expansion was $647,246 toward which the Duke Endowment and Mr. R.J. Reynolds, Jr. each contributed $150,000. Construction was completed in November 1941. Records indicate that the hospital trustees were still trying to raise an additional $150,000 one year later, but were having difficulty because of a competing campaign initiated by President Kitchin for enlargement of the campus at Wake Forest. During the war years special federal funds were available for hospital construction that related to civil defense. The suggestion that Baptist Hospital apply for assistance from this source was rejected on the principle of separation of church and state. This event sparked a denominational debate concerning the acceptance of federal funds for facilities, a debate not resolved until almost two decades later.

Medical School Facilities

The four trustees of the Bowman Gray Fund agreed to serve as an Advisory Council to the dean. They were Mr. James A. Gray, President of R.J. Reynolds Tobacco Company and brother of the late Bowman Gray; Mrs. Nathalie Gray Bernard, widow of Bowman Gray; and his two sons, Bowman and Gordon Gray. The last two joined the Army and Navy, respectively, in 1942, and James Gray became the key advisor. Dr. Carpenter stated in his history that this council advised on financial matters and overall development and "largely relieved the Wake Forest trustees of many perplexing problems the school faced" in its early years.

The accumulated dividends in the Bowman Gray bequest were used to buy 4,000 shares of Reynolds common stock, bringing the total to 18,000 with a value of $720,000. Using this stock as collateral, funds to construct and equip the first medical school building which totaled $444,881 were borrowed from the National Shawmut Bank of Boston at 1½% interest. A year later, Mr. James Gray arranged for the loan to be moved to the First National Bank of Atlanta at 1% interest. The securities, of course, were yielding far more than interest payments. As an historical note, forty-five years later this Atlanta bank merged with Wachovia Bank of Winston-Salem, which also played an important role in aiding the medical center in its development.

The original medical school facility was a six-story, 70,465-square-foot building directly connected to the North Carolina Baptist Hospital on the first through the fourth floors. It was designed to include space for the basic medical sciences, a library, clinical laboratories, animal quarters, a student lounge, photography and art, and administration. It was planned that the clinical faculty would be housed in a future wing and in hospital space. Because of limited finances and the ensuing events, the enlargement of the school was delayed until 1957.

Due to the uncertainty caused by the war in Europe, the architects for the medical school and hospital, Northup and O'Brien of Winston-Salem, were asked to speed up planning and construction. They indicated a completion date for the school, at best, of August 1941, just prior to its planned use for classes in September. However, due to restrictions on materials, a delay of up to three years was projected if the United States entered the war. An amphitheater for teaching was to be built adjacent to the power plant. Perhaps because of the urgency of completion of construction, its design was allegedly taken from a picture in a medical textbook of a traditional German operating amphitheater. Ground-breaking ceremonies were held in April 1940, and construction was begun the following July. The cornerstone was laid on April 16, 1941, and the medical school was moved from Wake Forest in June of that year. The move was accompanied by somewhat less than 2,500 volumes for the library, which served as the original holdings. Instruction began in September for 42 freshmen and 30 sophomores.

Faculty

In an attempt to forestall the opposition from local physicians which commonly occurs when a new medical school is established, Dr. Carpenter made a unique offer during an address to the Forsyth

County Medical Society on October 10, 1939. He invited every member to join the faculty of the school and requested that those who were interested complete personal information forms that were made available at the meeting. Dr. Wingate M. Johnson recounts that 63 physicians applied and were elected to the faculty by trustee action in May 1941. He indicated further that 28 actually helped teach in the school at some time.[3] Several years later, specialty board eligibility or certification was made a requirement for the continuation of these appointments with several years' grace given to attain such a status. However, this requirement was not enforced until after the end of World War II.

Nine full-time faculty in the basic sciences moved to Winston-Salem. These included stalwarts such as Camillo Artom (Biochemistry), Robert P. Morehead (Pathology) and Herbert M. Vann (Anatomy). Like Dean Carpenter, their loyalty to Wake Forest, their faith in the future, and their commitment to academic excellence formed a critically important contribution to the survival and growth of the medical center.

As noted, 63 practicing physicians in Winston-Salem were given clinical appointments to the faculty. Twelve were invited to move their offices to the school in the capacity of geographic full-time faculty and become members of the newly established Private Diagnostic Clinic (PDC) that was organized as a group practice to care for private patients. The existence of a separately organized PDC at Duke since 1931 had been accepted by the medical profession as differing from the corporate practice of medicine which was considered unethical at the time. As a similar model was used in Winston-Salem, there was apparently no dispute over this sensitive issue. Dr. Wingate M. Johnson, who had practiced medicine in Winston-Salem since 1910, served as chief of the clinic, and moved to the medical school in January 1942. He was followed in July by Drs. Fred K. and Robert R. Garvey (Urology), Dr. Leroy J. Butler (Pediatrics), Dr. James A. Harrill (Ear, Nose and Throat), Dr. Robert L. McMillan (Cardiology), Dr. Elbert A. MacMillan (Medicine and Psychiatry), Dr. Robert A. Moore (Orthopedics), and Drs. William H. Sprunt and Arthur deT. Valk (Surgery). The hospital employed Dr. J.P. Rousseau to direct Radiology and Dr. Roscoe L. Wall, Sr., to head Anesthesiology. Offices and examining rooms for the clinicians were provided on the first floor of the medical school building. The importance of these pioneers, the steady leadership of Dr. Johnson, and the organization and policies of the clinic itself cannot be over-emphasized. These clinicians left well-established practices in the community, they were provided only limited space and utilities, but committed themselves to give a considerable part of their time to academic activities without financial compensation. The school could not have survived without them. A number subsequently achieved national recognition in their fields, including Dr. Johnson, who excelled also as an author of several books and as editor of the *North Carolina Medical Journal*. He was the first physician from North Carolina elected to the Board of Trustees of the American Medical Association. He had served for many years as a Wake Forest trustee.

Mr. Clyde T. Hardy, who had recently earned the certificate in hospital administration at Duke University, was employed as the manager of the clinic in 1941 after his release from duty with the Navy. More will be said regarding his important contribution, not only to this phase of the school, but equally to the overall growth and development of the center, until his retirement in 1984.

With basic decisions completed on the medical school and clinical teaching facilities, augmentation of faculty was a high priority. Key clinical appointments included Tinsley Harrison, from Vanderbilt Medical School as chairman of the Department of Medicine; Howard H. Bradshaw, from Jefferson Medical College as chairman of the Department of Surgery; Frank R. Lock from Tulane as chairman of the Department of Obstetrics and Gynecology; George T. Harrell from Duke as assistant professor of Medicine; and Robert B. Lawson from the University of Rochester School of Medicine as assistant professor of Pediatrics. Among this group, only Dr. Harrison had an established academic and scientific record, though in later years each of the others became nationally recognized for their academic and scientific contributions. Two equally important appointments filled much needed leadership gaps in the basic sciences. Dr. J. Maxwell Little of Vanderbilt joined the faculty before the move from Wake Forest and carried the major responsibility in pharmacology. Dr. Harold D. Green from Western Reserve replaced Dr. Herbert Wells as chairman of the Department of Physiology and Pharmacology in 1944. It is noteworthy that all of these appointees were young men, most of whom had only recently completed their advanced training in their specialties. They were drawn to Bowman Gray by the challenge and unique opportunities afforded by a new school, and not, as attested in the budget, by an attractive salary.

Medical School Finances

The fiscal constraint under which the school began operation is reflected in its financial statement for 1941–1942. Total income was $184,590, with expenditures of $181,774. Income included $33,209 from tuition paid by 42 freshmen and 30 sophomores, $38,460 from the Bowman Gray Fund that was treated as endowment, and $5,000 from Wake Forest College. The last was increased to $40,287 the next year, and then fixed at $22,450 per year representing the yearly net amount the school was receiving from the college before the move to Winston-Salem. The debt on the building was $431,187, and only interest payments were made during the first five years. A serious crisis occurred in 1942 when a decline in the price of Reynolds securities brought them below the 25% margin required by the bank loan. Bowman and Gordon Gray loaned the medical school 6,000 shares of Reynolds stock and $22,800 in cash to satisfy this requirement.

Hospital-Medical School Agreements

It is appropriate at this juncture to outline the major principles in the original affiliation agreement between the college and Baptist Hospital, dated November 30, 1939.[4] These principles formed a sound basis for two separate corporations to function together initially as an academic medical center.

The document, a Memorandum of Understanding, assigned the responsibility for professional services in the hospital to the medical school. The heads of clinical departments were named heads of their respective hospital services. A faculty appointment was required before staff privileges were granted. A medical director was provided for, who was to be a member of the faculty elected by the hospital trustees on the recommendation of the dean, and was responsible for the professional administration of the hospital. Dr. Carpenter himself served in this capacity during the initial years. The attending and resident staff were to be appointed by the hospital trustees on the recommendation of the dean and the hospital staff executive committee, which included the hospital administrator. Those appointments included pathology, radiology and anesthesiology. As such, the hospital was to have a closed staff which would allow the control of professional and academic standards by the school of medicine.

The administrator of the hospital was charged with the business administration of that institution, which included property, finances and conduct of nurses, dieticians and all others not having direct responsibility for patient care.

Further, it was understood specifically that the medical school was financially responsible for its operation, and the hospital was responsible for its maintenance. Items of joint expense were a joint responsibility and the proportionate shares were to be decided by the dean and hospital administrator. If they failed to agree, the two trustee bodies would decide on the proper division of costs.

Several other important policies were soon developed that were basic to the academic center. All hospital patients were to be utilized for teaching unless this was judged by the attending physician to jeopardize the health of the patient. All fees for professional services were to be billed and collected centrally through the Private Diagnostic Clinic. The clinic had its own chief and executive committee, which included the dean. From the beginning, the medical school owned and operated the clinical laboratory services, though in 1956 ownership was turned over to the hospital.

The Honorable Odus M. Mull

The important role of Odus Mull in the establishment and early development of the medical center needs special note. Mull was born on September 18, 1880 in rural Cleveland County, North Carolina. He attended Wake Forest College, receiving the A.B. degree in 1902 and the LL.B. degree in 1903. He became associated in the practice of law in Shelby with O. Max Gardner, Clyde R. Hoey and James and Yates Webb. This group was very active in the political life of North Carolina and became known as the "Shelby Dynasty." Gardner and Hoey became governors, and Mull served six terms in the House of Representatives and was Speaker of the House in 1941. He introduced and obtained passage of the legislation establishing vocational education in this state. He became widely known as a master politician; served as chairman of the State Democratic party 1928–1933, and was called by many "the maker of governors." Mull was also an active and influential Baptist. He served as a trustee of Baptist Hospital during the formation of the medical center and as a trustee of Wake Forest College at the time of its move to Winston-Salem.

Mention has been made of Mull's important role in the Hoey

Commission and as liaison between the Gray family and the administration of Wake Forest that resulted in the founding of the medical center. All during the early development phase, he also served as an influential and highly respected advocate of the center among the Baptist constituency. As a hospital trustee he played a key role in obtaining the grant from the Duke Endowment for the enlargement of the hospital, and in the recruitment of the first trained hospital administrator to Baptist Hospital, Ray E. Brown, also from Shelby, in 1943. Throughout this early phase of development he was advisor and confidante to the dean. Later, as a trustee of Wake Forest College, he aided significantly in its move to Winston-Salem. A sampling of his correspondence to Dr. Carpenter reflects the pragmatic optimism and wise counsel that was characteristic of this unusual man. Shortly after the meeting with the trustees of the Bowman Gray Fund in 1938, Mull wrote, "I feel that you and Dr. Kitchin were slightly disappointed because we did not have immediate prospect of the total minimum requirements for a four-year medical school. That would be too good. Our penurious nervous system couldn't stand that much at one time." On borrowing when additional debt was contemplated: "It is better to pay and borrow again than never pay." On a budget submission by the medical school requesting additional funds from the college trustees, "Giant oaks from little acorns grow; however, considerable faith is required to reinforce our confidence that these funds can and will be supplied." When asked in 1944 to go to Washington to seek federal financial aid to build a nurses home for Baptist Hospital, he wrote, "I am anxious to render every assistance possible, but prefer to spend our time and energy where there is reasonable prospect of accomplishing something." Finally, advice and encouragement to the dean during that same year—a period that Dr. Carpenter referred to as the "dark days"—"The most successful man is not always the fellow who can do the most work himself, but the fellow who can select and secure the most efficient help to do all the different jobs. After this is done, the job of keeping them at it and making such changes as time requires is a man-sized job. I believe you are making progress. Take courage and continue to go forward. The momentum obtained will help overcome the many difficulties that will constantly present themselves."

Odus Mull died in 1962 and a portrait presented by his family hangs in an honored place in the medical center in remembrance of his many contributions and the unique role he played in its early history.

Retrospect

Looking back on the environment and the financial resources that existed at the time of the establishment of this academic medical center, one can only echo Dr. Carpenter's remark later that the decision was based solely on faith. The time was the prelude to the entry of the United States into World War II; the medical school was to be separated from its parent by 110 miles; funds available for medical school facilities and operations were well below minimum; and no additional financial help was available from the college. National foundations refused start-up assistance and the reaction of leaders in medical education and many local physicians to the plan was negative.

On the other hand, some critically important positive elements were present. These included the leadership of a determined dean who believed the plan would succeed, a heritage of high standards and a core faculty of remarkable young men supplemented by a group of excellent local clinicians who formed a cooperative group practice and were willing to gamble on the future without institutional compensation. In addition, the medical school had a highly respected advisory group including James A. Gray and Odus Mull, and the enthusiastic cooperation of the Baptist Hospital trustees, who were willing to expand that institution and endorse sound principles of affiliation.

At the first medical school commencement in 1943, Dr. Frederick M. Hanes, professor of Medicine at Duke University School of Medicine, received an honorary Doctor of Science degree from Wake Forest, recommended by the Bowman Gray School of Medicine. At that ceremony, he stated, "In 1941, I knew damned well that it couldn't be done. . . . Now that it has been done, I don't believe it."[5] Years later it was truly said that in developing the medical center a shoe was built around a shoestring.[6]

References and Notes

1. News Notes, Journal of the Association of American Medical Colleges 14: 334, September 1939.
2. North Carolina Baptist Hospital Enlargement Campaign brochure, 1939.
3. Johnson, Wingate M. Unpublished History of the Bowman Gray School of Medicine.
4. Memorandum of Understanding between the Trustees of Wake Forest College and the North Carolina Baptist Hospitals, Inc., November 30, 1939.
5. Davis, Chester. Bowman Gray School: A Medical Miracle, feature story, Winston-Salem Journal and Sentinel, September 10, 1961.
6. *Ibid.*

CHAPTER III

The Fight for Survival—
The Decade of the Forties

The War Years (1941–1945)

During 1940, national defense activity in this country accelerated due to the expanding conflict in Europe. In October of that year, the Association of American Medical Colleges (AAMC) established a committee on Medical College Preparedness to deal with federal departments on matters that related to medical students and faculty. It was evident that, if the United States entered the war, a shortage of physicians available to the armed forces and civilian population was a serious possibility and, as such, training programs needed to be protected. Draft deferments were arranged for premedical and medical students and essential faculty. In July 1941, the AAMC urged schools that could do so to increase their enrollment by ten percent and initiated a study on an accelerated curriculum. In October, third- and fourth-year medical students were urged to apply for reserve commissions in the armed services. The United States entered the war on December 8, three months after the first classes at Bowman Gray began instruction in Winston-Salem. It is of interest that, because of the rapid decline in the number of law students not deferred from the draft, Wake Forest and Duke University Law Schools merged their classes between 1943 and 1946.

A memorandum from the AAMC sent to the deans of all medical colleges on December 18, 1941 strongly urged every school to initiate immediately a four-quarter per year accelerated program and to review its list of faculty members who were essential for teaching and research. Both activities were considered part of the national defense program. The Bowman Gray School of Medicine complied immediately

31

with these requests. This meant a new class was to be accepted and one graduated every nine months.

The school at that time was accredited for only two years of medical education. The dean expressed concern to Dr. Fred Zapffe, secretary of the AAMC, that under these circumstances as students progressed to their junior and senior years they might not be protected from the draft. Zapffe replied that Bowman Gray was on the official list of medical schools supplied to the federal government; since the list made no mention of two-year schools, this should insure the safety of students in all years. The first junior class began in June 1942; the school was inspected a year later, and was approved in November 1943, one month before the first class of 31 students graduated.

The war years posed difficulties in recruiting faculty for the clinical years and in obtaining equipment for hospitals and medical schools. Fortunately, essential equipment had been delivered to the school and hospital, and several key full-time faculty appointments from outside Winston-Salem had been made in 1940 and early 1941. These included Tinsley Harrison, George T. Harrell, Arthur Grollman, and John Williams in Medicine; Frank R. Lock in Obstetrics and Gynecology; Howard H. Bradshaw, in Surgery; and William Allan, a nationally known geneticist who headed a $50,000 research program financed by the Carnegie Foundation. The accelerated curriculum and the loss of local physicians and several faculty members to the armed forces sharply increased the educational and patient care load at the medical center. However, the faculty voted to do "double duty" rather than recruit additional members who might not meet standards or who were needed in their local communities for civilian practice.

The accelerated curriculum eliminated the long summer vacations that many students used to earn funds to help support their medical education. Loan funds available from the school were almost nonexistent, though a federal loan program was established later. However, in December 1942 the federal government initiated the Army Specialized Training Program (ASTP) and the Navy V-12 program under which students eligible for military duty were given inactive commissions, uniforms and $132 per month as pay and living allowance. The school was paid the cost of student tuition, fees and equipment. All graduates were allowed a nine-month internship and one-third of those an additional nine to eighteen months of residency training before active military duty. This was known as the 9-9-9 program. Although the school retained complete control of the educational process, the program was supplemented by military instruction and weekly drills under Army and Navy personnel assigned locally. Dr. Wingate Johnson later wrote, and many in academic medicine agreed, that the accelerated program lowered the quality of training and the only advantage was not having hot weather graduation exercises. He also quipped that the dubious advantage of the military financial assistance programs was to encourage students to get married during medical school.

The Baptist Hospital School of Nursing also participated in the accelerated training effort by expanding its student body and adopting an accelerated curriculum under the Nurse Cadet Program financed by the U. S. Public Health Service. One hundred fifteen of the 122 students were accepted into this program. They received uniforms and salaries of $15 to $20 per month, and the hospital received reimbursement for their tuition and maintenance. In return, students agreed to remain active in military or civilian nursing for the duration of the war. By 1944 additional programs had been established at the medical center for training dieticians, nurse anesthetists and x-ray and medical technologists.

The war proved that hospitals could use auxiliary aid to great advantage. As the supply of nurses became depleted, experiments were begun with hospital aides who later became the first licensed practical nurses in North Carolina by state waiver. Countless hours of valuable service were given also by the Red Cross gray ladies and girl scouts during this period of nurse shortage.

To meet the needs of the expanding nurse student body, the hospital trustees in November 1943 authorized a major expansion of the three-story nurses home. It was to be financed by a Federal Works Administration grant related to the Nurse Cadet program and by loans. The grant award of $63,000 was accepted by the trustees "in the public interest" with three dissenting votes; however, the Baptist State Convention met in Winston-Salem in 1943 and soundly rejected the acceptance of this grant, authorizing the hospital to borrow $110,000 for the project. Construction was completed in March 1945 at a cost of $131,500 with the help of approximately $21,500 generated from government funds received from housing the nurse cadets. The facility allowed space for 72 more nurses and classroom areas and brought the total enrollment to 150.

In February 1943, the hospital was completely occupied and waiting lists for admission had been established. Outpatient space for service patients had become totally inadequate. The number of service inpatients had increased to 31 percent and the clinical faculty was experiencing difficulty in getting beds for private patients. As a result, a bed quota for each member of the Private Diagnostic Clinic was established in January 1945, with a maximum of five assigned to the senior faculty. The trustees authorized the appointment of a building committee chaired by Mr. Irving E. Carlyle, and an advisory committee of the professional staff to study the need for expansion. Schmidt, Garden and Erickson was employed to assist in developing architectural plans. In April 1944, a plan for a new outpatient facility and an addition to the hospital with 320 beds to bring the total to 560, was approved. A committee, chaired by Mr. Odus Mull, was appointed to raise the necessary funds, estimated at $2.5 million. However, an expansion of the hospital was delayed until 1952 because of a series of events that ultimately brought Wake Forest College to Winston-Salem in 1956.

In September 1944 the construction of a two-story outpatient building with a capacity for 45,000 patient visits was approved to be located next to the new nurses home and directly connected to the hospital. The building was completed in July 1946 at a cost of $230,000 and financed through a mix of grants and funds from Duke Endowment, industry, individuals and the Cooperative Program of the Baptist State Convention. It contained 48 examining rooms, departments of physiotherapy and dentistry, a brace shop, and special equipment for urology and ophthalmology.

The complexity of operating a teaching hospital under the pressures of patient demands during wartime occupied much of the time of the dean (who was serving also as medical director), as the hospital superintendent was involved to a great extent in public relations activities among the Baptist constituency. The trustees recognized the need for a well-trained hospital administrator. Odus Mull recommended Mr. Ray E. Brown, who was appointed administrator on June 20, 1943. Brown was a native of Shelby, North Carolina, and a recent graduate of the University of Chicago School of Hospital Administration. Mr. Smith Hagaman resigned in January 1945 and the position of superintendent was discontinued.

Meanwhile, several important changes had occurred in the faculty. Dr. Tinsley Harrison resigned in March 1944 to accept the deanship at Southwestern Medical School in Dallas, Texas, and Arthur Grollman joined him six months later. Both had contributed greatly to the early recognition of the school through their productive research programs and the fame of Dr. Harrison as a highly effective teacher. Dr. George T. Harrell, Jr., who had developed innovative approaches to medical education and was becoming recognized for his research in infectious disease, was appointed chairman of the Department of Medicine. Dr. William Allan died in April 1943 and Dr. C. Nash Herndon, who had served as his fellow, carried on the genetics research program. In addition, Herndon became director of the new Outpatient Department when the facility opened in 1946.

A comprehensive report summarizing the first five years of operation of the medical school was submitted by the dean to the college president, the local advisory board, and trustees of Wake Forest College on June 30, 1945, just as the war was coming to a close. It included a status report on Baptist Hospital by the administrator.

The medical school was admitting 50 students per class, and allocating two-thirds of the places to students from North Carolina, South Carolina, Virginia and eastern Tennessee. There were 62 active faculty, of whom 11 were in the basic sciences—"the same number that made up the faculty of the two-year school at Wake Forest five years ago." Eleven of the clinical faculty had been brought in from other schools. From the listing of faculty publications, the major research contributions came from the departments of Biochemistry, Pathology and Medicine, and involved Drs. Camillo Artom, Robert P. Morehead, Tinsley Harrison and George Harrell. The organization of the school followed the usual pattern. The dean was responsible for final decisions on operations and was advised by a council consisting of the eight heads of departments and the hospital administrator. The council met once monthly, at night occasionally over dinner at the Robert E. Lee Hotel. There were faculty committees responsible for admissions, curriculum, and promotions for each of the four classes. Faculty appointments for full-time and part-time positions were made either with limited or unlimited tenure, and approved by the college president and trustees. The most important criteria for faculty promotion were defined as a person's contribution to the advancement of knowledge in his field, followed by teaching and administrative abilities, and proficiency in the practice of one's specialty. The stress on research and publication was directly related to the desire to enhance the reputation of the school nationally.

The first trained medical librarian was employed in March 1944. She was Mary Ament from Birmingham, Alabama. Nell Benton, who

35

had received library experience at Woman's College of the University of North Carolina, later UNC-Greensboro, was named assistant librarian. The library budget for the year was $7,530. Ament resigned in 1945 and Benton was given her responsibilities. Benton's report to the dean described the library in 1944 as in a chaotic condition. Following a complete reorganization and elimination of irrelevant material the total volumes that remained were approximately 6,500. Current journals totaled 261 with 119 obtained through regular subscription, 44 through gifts, 104 through exchanges of the *North Carolina Medical Journal*, edited by Wingate Johnson, and the *Journal of the Bowman Gray School of Medicine*. Interlibrary loan and microfilm services had been established and an historical collection begun. Highest priority was given to the completion of journal back files. Nell Benton resigned in 1963 after 19 years of loyal and dedicated service to marry a former faculty member. She was replaced in February 1963 by Miss Elizabeth Withrow, who had served as librarian at the State University of New York in Buffalo.

Medical School expenditure for 1944–1945 was $299,512, up from $181,774 four years earlier; $108,000 was from tuition and the remainder was income from the original Bowman Gray gift, the college, grants, and sales and services. Only interest payments had been made on the original debt of $431,187. The budget did not include fees for services to patients received by the clinical faculty, which were collected through the Private Diagnostic Clinic, although it is noted that these amounted to $209,302 during 1944. It is of interest that, contrary to prevailing opinion, the only financial benefit of the wartime programs to the school was the increase in tuition income generated by the accelerated curriculum, which amounted to less than $20,000 per year.

The dean concluded in his report that the school had the smallest staff of any medical school in the United States, had no departments of Preventive Medicine, Psychiatry, Physical Therapy, Dermatology, Neurology, or Pharmacology, and had reached its peak of accomplishment with its present resources. A study by department directors placed budgetary needs at $602,198. Adding professional fees generated to the present basic income, this left a deficit of $171,529. He urged that a development program be started at once, noting that the average life of the five extinct medical schools in North Carolina was ten years. There is no question that this stark report brought subsequent action, as will be seen.

In contrast, Dr. Carpenter praised the trustees of the hospital for their progressive program, the new administrator for his ability, leadership and wisdom, and stated that the joint operation was being conducted in a most harmonious and satisfactory manner. The hospital showed a favorable operating status with a cash balance at the end of March 1945 of $33,000 with all current obligations paid. Total assets of the hospital were $998,242, and the plant fund had liabilities of $177,000. During that year 7,484 patients were admitted, of whom 40 percent were from Forsyth County. Bradshaw reported that among the 1,665 major operations the most common in order of frequency were ostectomy-sequestrectomy, appendectomy without drainage, prostatectomy, craniotomy-decompression, thyroidectomy and enterostomy-gastrostomy.[1] It is notable also that the average cost per patient day was $7.90.

The war in Europe ended in May 1945 and with Japan in August of that year.

Early Curriculum Experiments

There was growing concern among medical educators at this time that the growth in medical knowledge and specialization was resulting in a separation of the preclinical and clinical sciences which was detrimental to the program of medical education. Further, many felt that subject emphasis in the traditional curriculum lacked proper balance. The young faculty at Bowman Gray believed that a new school without established vested interests offered a unique opportunity to correct these deficiencies. Early experiments in the integration of the basic and clinical sciences were described by Harrell and Vann in 1945.[2] These included clinical correlation clinics each Saturday morning for first- and second-year students, participation in basic science courses by clinicians (including residents), basic science reinforcement in the junior and senior years, and weekly clinico-pathologic conferences for all students and faculty. The authors felt that success rested on the attitude with which correlation was approached and the aptitude of the individual instructor. They indicated that the "pure" or average clinician did not make an effective correlation teacher.

Two years later Carpenter published a follow-up report.[3] He stated that the Bowman Gray experience with the integrated curriculum had been satisfactory, particularly at the horizontal level; however, proper balance in subject matter had not been achieved. As such, the school, through a reorganization of departments, was placing the entire curriculum under four divisions—Structure, Function, Medicine and Surgery. Each division had a chairman who served as a coordinator and was responsible for maintaining proper balance in emphasis among the various subjects in his division and with other division chairmen in planning correlation between divisions. The heads of the respective departments were termed directors and continued to be responsible directly to the dean on all other matters.

Recently, Harrell wrote that Dr. Tinsley Harrison was the first to propose the division organization to improve correlation of the curriculum, but at that time the proposal raised administrative tensions.[4] Records are not clear on the impact of this division system, but it was abandoned in the mid-1950s. However, correlated teaching of the basic sciences did survive in many areas of the educational program. These early experiments served to focus the attention of the faculty on the process of medical education. The major problem in achieving a fully integrated curriculum during this period appears to have been limitations in the size and the diversity of the faculty and the time required for other activities. The concept itself was sound and was more fully conceptualized and implemented by Western Reserve University School of Medicine beginning in 1952.

Peacetime Begins

Nationally, the immediate postwar challenges to academic medical centers involved deceleration of the teaching program and providing educational opportunities for returning physician veterans. The Army Specialized Training and V-12 Programs were discontinued and internships increased to 12-month programs in July 1946. Medical schools were authorized to return to a four-year program in the fall of that year. There were approximately 55,000 medical officers in the armed forces, and 80% of those who replied to a questionnaire of the American Medical Association indicated they wanted three months to two years of additional training. The North Carolina schools and cooperating hospitals expanded opportunities to accommodate many of the 674 expected North Carolina veterans. Special emphasis was given to those who had graduated between 1939 and 1944, a group that Duke's Dean Davison termed in his history "the lost generation." The GI Bill of Rights allowed financial assistance through the Veterans Administration to physicians whose education was interrupted by service, and gave added support to medical schools for each veteran accepted in residency status.

The medical school took advantage of the war surplus supply program of the federal government by first obtaining "veterans education living quarters." The 24 housing units were located behind the school and became known affectionately as "splinter village." Later a surplus laundry, dishwasher, surgical instruments and a truck were obtained for the hospital.

Ray Brown resigned as administrator of the Baptist Hospital in September 1945 to become assistant superintendent of the University of Chicago Hospitals and Clinics, which he later headed. Mr. Reid T. Holmes, who completed his training in hospital administration at Duke in 1940 and had served since that time as assistant superintendent of Duke Hospital, was employed in November 1945 to replace Brown. This began 25 years of productive and continuous service to the medical center by a man who was concerned not only with the integrity of the medical center, but also with the welfare of its patients and employees.

The candid report of the dean to the trustees and local advisory board regarding the status of the medical school at the end of five years was supplemented by a letter to the chairman of the trustee committee of the college indicating that it was James Gray's belief that, if some reduction in the principal on the demand note at the First National Bank in Atlanta were not made soon, the credit of Wake Forest College would be jeopardized. This communication stimulated the college trustees to make payments over three years of $50,000 on the principal and to appoint a trustee committee for the school with power to act. The committee was chaired by Irving E. Carlyle, a distinguished lawyer in Winston-Salem.

Meanwhile, in 1946, Bowman and Gordon Gray had returned from military duty and established trusts of $125,000 each to help initiate Departments of Neuropsychiatry and Preventive Medicine. The funds were to be expended over a five-year period. Dr. Thomas T. Mackie, a specialist in tropical medicine from New York City, and once personal physician of Mrs. Nathalie Gray Bernard, was selected to head the Department of Preventive Medicine and Tropical Medicine. He was joined by his wife Janet, a British physician who had had extensive medical experience in Africa.

Beginning in 1940 Mrs. Bernard had deeded several parcels of land and several small buildings at the Graylyn estate to the medical school that were used by the school to house animals for research. In 1945 she deeded the manor house with additional land and gave funds to help renovate the mansion for a 30-bed neuropsychiatric hospital. Dr. Lloyd J. Thompson from Yale Medical School was selected to head the department and operate Graylyn Hospital, which was opened in 1947.

Dr. Carpenter had reported by letter to President Kitchin in 1942 that he had learned, in talks with Mr. L. D. Long, secretary to Mr. William Neal Reynolds, that Mr. Reynolds was interested in seeing Wake Forest College move to Winston-Salem. Dr. Kitchin did not reply, but soon initiated a plan to expand the college at Wake Forest. The Baptist Convention "heartily endorsed" his plans and a $7 million fund-raising campaign began in November 1945. Dr. Carpenter wrote that as an eastern North Carolinian President Kitchin strongly opposed the move to Winston-Salem and was determined to upset the movement by "sprinkling the campus with buildings and then the College can't move." Dr. Kitchin later realized that the move was inevitable and strongly supported it in a statement to the trustees in 1946 entitled "Wake Forest College Looking Forward."

Funds from the Veterans Administration for house staff training temporarily offset loss of tuition due to curriculum deceleration, but overcrowding of the hospital limited the admission of private patients and thus funds to support additional faculty. Physicians associated with the Private Diagnostic Clinic pledged $200,000 toward the construction of a 150-bed South Wing for the hospital if space would also be provided for their ambulatory patient practice. The Baptist Convention delayed approval of the request of the hospital trustees to borrow $400,000 toward this expansion until November 1946, and then conditioned borrowing on first raising the remaining funds needed. It was reported to the convention in 1947 that leaders in Winston-Salem had requested that the hospital trustees not expand on the existing site, but urged them, with the college trustees, to make a serious attempt to move the hospital and medical school to the Graylyn estate. This request occurred shortly after the Z. Smith Reynolds Foundation and Charles H. and Mary Reynolds Babcock had offered operational support for the college and 300 acres of the Reynolda estate adjacent to Graylyn, respectively, if the college were to move to Winston-Salem. It was proposed that a 600-bed hospital and a medical school twice the existing size be built on the Graylyn estate for an estimated cost of $6,280,000. To finance the project, the existing plant was to be sold to a group of local businessmen for $1.8 million; $400,000 would come from the convention, $200,000 from the Private Diagnostic Clinic staff pledge, and $3.88 million would be raised from private sources in a program coordinated with the college.

In its report to the convention in 1948, the hospital trustees stated that it had been brought to their attention that the additional funds being raised by Wake Forest to make the move of the college possible were short of the goal, that a campaign by the hospital could seriously affect the outcome and, as such, fund raising was being postponed. Finally, in July 1949, the trustees decided in favor of further development of the hospital in its present location as the potential for the move to Graylyn had not materialized.

In December 1946 James A. Gray, then president of R.J. Reynolds Tobacco Company and close advisor to the dean, established an irrevocable trust of $1.7 million, of which 18/35ths was to benefit the medical school. He stipulated that the income from the medical school's share (approximately $30,000 per year) was to be used first to liquidate the note at the First National Bank in Atlanta, and then could be used for the "general furtherance and improvement of education and research." This wise and beneficent gift and the original Bowman Gray Fund that was held intact served as early endowments and are now valued at more than $6.7 million.

The affiliations of the medical school with the County Hospital and Methodist Children's Home were very successful. However, the use of the Junior League Hospital for teaching proved to be impractical. A Child Guidance Clinic that had been located there was moved to a house on Lockland Avenue near the center, but its value to the school was limited and the clinic was closed two years later because of a lack of common philosophy between the director and the local sponsors. In 1944, the Roaring Gap Hospital that had been built and financed by James A. Gray was closed because of a shortage of nurses. It was sold for $16,500 and the proceeds were given to the medical school as the Leroy J. Butler Endowment for research in medicine.

A key administrative appointment at the medical school was made in 1947. Mr. Harry O. Parker, a certified public accountant from Raleigh, replaced Mr. Stuart Warnken as controller. His loyal and valuable service in helping to maintain financial solvency of the institution extended through 1971 when he suffered a stroke. After his recovery he was called back in 1975 and served part-time as treasurer of the new Medical Center Corporation until his death in 1983.

At the end of this momentous decade the medical school had adjusted to a peace-time program, but continued to suffer from severe budgetary constraints. The major fund-raising campaign of the college to assist in its move to Winston-Salem greatly limited fund raising by the medical center. Faculty recruitment was difficult because of low basic science salary scales and restrictions on professional income due to the shortage of hospital beds. Town and gown tensions had been stimulated by activation of the policy that part-time clinical faculty appointments (and admitting privileges to Baptist Hospital) would be continued only for physicians who were eligible for, or certified by, the boards in their specialty. The original plan to double the size of the medical school facilities had been delayed; however, some space had been added to the fifth floor to house academic offices for psychiatry, an isotope laboratory and the Institute of Tropical Medicine. The space for the institute was financed by a gift of $300,000 from Mr. W. B. Woolworth of New York. Mr. Woolworth supported the research of the Mackies for his company, the West Indies Sugar Corporation, in the Dominican Republic and Cuba.

Under the prevailing circumstances, faculty recruitment was restricted primarily to promising young men and women who were interested in the opportunities afforded by a new school. Some remained for only short periods, while others stayed and made important and lasting contributions to its academic and clinical programs. During this immediate postwar period these included Eben Alexander (Neurosurgery), Ernest H. Yount (Medicine), Richard L. Burt (Obstetrics-Gynecology), Richard L. Masland (Neurology), Weston M. Kelsey (Pediatrics), R. Winston Roberts (Ophthalmology), James F. Martin (Radiology), Henry L. Valk (Medicine), Lucile W. Hutaff (Preventive Medicine/Medicine), and Richard C. Proctor (Psychiatry).

This was indeed a time that the loyalty and dedication of a group of outstanding faculty members was demonstrated. Time and again these men and women placed the best interests of the school above those of their departments or themselves and, with the dean, continued their faith in the future. Needless to say, the financial support of the Gray family was a major contribution to the survival of the school during this difficult first decade.

References and Notes

1. Carpenter, C. C. Report on the First Five Years of Operation and Recommendations to the President, Advisory Council and Board of Trustees. June 30, 1945.
2. Harrell, G. T. and Vann, H. M. Correlation of the medical curriculum. J. Assoc. Am Med Coll 20:139–151, 1945.
3. Carpenter, C. C. Integration and organization of medical curriculum. J. Assoc. Am Med Coll 22:30–37, 1947.
4. Harrell, G. T. The early years at Bowman Gray, N C Med J 44:805–807 (Dec) 1983.

CHAPTER IV

Solidifying the Base—
the Decade of the Fifties

The Changing Environment

Federal health policies that were legislated beginning in the late 1940s and implemented during the next two decades had a major impact on the development of academic medical centers. The social role, scope of programs and services, and facilities of these institutions greatly expanded, as did the complexity of financing and administration. Congress declared that the support of biomedical research was a proper federal responsibility and wisely recognized this could be best accomplished in partnership with universities through a peer-reviewed grants mechanism that supported not only research, but also the training of future investigators and the expansion of research facilities and supporting services. Appropriations for these purposes grew rapidly under the unprecedented political leadership of Senator Lister Hill, Congressman John Fogarty and James Shannon, director of the National Institutes of Health. This was accomplished through the categorical disease approach used so successfully in fund raising by private agencies such as the American Heart Association and American Cancer Society.

The Hill-Burton program was established in the late 1940s to improve geographic access to hospital care. Federal grants to states helped to stimulate a proliferation of small hospitals, particularly in rural areas, and assist in the expansion of existing institutions. As hospital costs escalated, private health insurance programs became well-established fringe benefits for employees within business and industry. Through the expanding largess of all of these programs, biomedical research and more advanced patient care were added to health manpower education as primary functions of academic medical centers. Termed the "three-legged stool," concern soon shifted to debate over the proper balance of these functions within each institution.

Deitrick and Berson completed an extensive study of medical schools in the United States at midcentury that was sponsored jointly by the Council on Medical Education and Hospitals of the American Medical Association and the Association of American Medical Colleges.[1] They noted that postwar increases in inflation and taxation had eroded finances and levels of philanthropy. The fundamental sciences upon which medical education depended were expanding rapidly and placed different demands on premedical and professional education. Medical schools were accepting larger classes and taking responsibility for training increasing numbers of interns, residents and allied health personnel. The need for refresher and specialty training by returning veterans had escalated. Teaching hospitals carried heavy loads of charity care without proper reimbursement. Biomedical research was concentrated primarily in the well-established and endowed institutions. The survey also found many medical schools that were not prepared to cope with these added responsibilities either financially or administratively. However, the authors noted a healthy ferment toward institutional improvement generated by these pressures and the presence of many thoughtful faculty members and administrators committed to the "principles at the heart of true medical education." They predicted that these important factors would set the proper course for the academic medical centers in the future.

Unfortunately, local circumstances did not allow the Bowman Gray School of Medicine or North Carolina Baptist Hospital to take early advantage of expanding federal financing for research or facilities. These included severe limitations on medical school space and hospital beds, the Baptist Convention's policies preventing the acceptance of federal funds for facilities, and restrictions placed on medical school fund raising because of the college campaign under way for the move to Winston-Salem.

The Priority of 1950

Despite these circumstances, the most pressing need of the center continued to be expansion of bed capacity for private patients through the addition of the South Wing of the hospital. This 150-bed facility was needed urgently to help meet patient demand and also to increase income from professional services. This income would allow much-needed additions to the clinical faculty which could then better balance patient care and academic responsibilities.

As mentioned before, the Baptist State Convention in 1946 committed itself to borrow for the hospital an amount not to exceed $400,000 toward the construction of the proposed South Wing, provided the hospital raised the additional amount needed. The hospital trustees did not pursue this plan because fund raising would conflict with the Wake Forest campaign; however, this delay had increased cost estimates. In November 1949 the trustees learned that federal funds were available for hospital construction under the Hill-Burton program through the North Carolina Medical Care Commission. A grant application was submitted and the commission committed $697,356 to the project provided that the hospital raise the additional funds. In December of that year, the trustees requested the General Board of the convention to approve the grant and additional financing, which included the $400,000 borrowing approved in 1946 (to be paid back through the hospital's share of the Cooperative Program); $200,000 pledged by the members of the Private Diagnostic Clinic and $400,000 to be raised from Winston-Salem friends for a total of $1.7 million. In addition to the 150 beds, the wing was to include a relocated and enlarged kitchen, employee dining room, and x-ray department. The General Board in special session approved the request by a vote of 21 to 12, with the proviso that "funds granted by the Commission be repaid in services rendered."

Questions were raised following this action and, at the regular meeting of the general board in January 1950, a resolution was passed requesting that the hospital trustees hold funds on hand for the project. A Committee of Fifteen from the General Board of the Baptist State Convention was appointed to study the matter of acceptance of federal grants by *both* the hospital and medical school, and a special convention was authorized four months later to hear the report and recommend action.

The basic problem involved the interpretation of the historic Baptist principle of the separation of church and state, which embodied the belief that tax subsidy leads to control by the state; and where there is control, freedom and separation cannot exist. The constitution of the convention, however, qualified this position and allowed an

47

"exchange of values" under circumstances where definite and full services are rendered.

The special convention was held in Charlotte on April 27, 1950. The Committee of Fifteen felt that the convention was morally and legally obligated by the action of the General Board at its December meeting, and recommended acceptance of the grant from the Medical Care Commission. However, after extensive debate the convention voted to instruct the hospital trustees not to accept the grant, designated two "Hospital expansion days" to receive voluntary contributions for the project through the churches, and recommended that a loan be authorized in the amount necessary to construct the South Wing. A Committee of Twenty-one was appointed to further study past and present practices of the institutions of the convention in their relationship to agencies of the state and federal governments.

Construction on the South Wing was begun in October 1951 and completed in 1954; however, an additional $280,000 was required to provide the necessary furnishings and equipment. The R.J. Reynolds Tobacco Company made two gifts to the project totaling $475,000 and the Duke Endowment gave a grant of $175,000. The hospital trustees reported in November 1955 that the $700,000 pledged to the South Wing by the Charlotte convention to replace government funds had been received in full.

The Church-State Issue and the Medical School

The Committee of Twenty-one reported to the annual Baptist State Convention in November 1950. Information from their institutions and agencies revealed a variety of state and federal subsidies, including government-donated buildings, war asset properties, G(overnment) I(ssue) aid to colleges, welfare funds for the care of indigents, research grants and the like. They indicated that there were areas of services or activities involving the exchange of values in which cooperation may occur between church and state, or the agencies of either, especially since individuals owe allegiance to both. They believed cooperation was possible without surrendering principles if the following conditions were met. Cooperative exchanges must be free of any control, direct or implied. They must represent genuine exchange of values, mutually agreed upon and so stated in a contract. Such exchanges should be consummated within reasonable time, but not to exceed two years; and such exchanges should be reported to the convention annually.

Regarding research grants, they recommended that any buildings, equipment or materials remaining at the end of the project should revert to the government or be sold at auction in which the institution could participate as a bidder. They recommended that the medical school accept no funds from government for medical education without prior approval of the convention and that future capital needs of all institutions related to the convention come from other than government sources.

Until 1957, as will be discussed later, those strict conditions posed problems for the medical school by restricting access to funds from federal programs supporting medical education and the expansion of research facilities. Research grants were handled within the stated policy by noting that they involved short-term services rendered under a clearly defined contract with the only requirements of the government being those related to fiscal accountability. All grants were reported annually by the medical school to the president of Wake Forest, assuming that communication of such information to the convention should be through him. Equipment purchased through research grants legally belonged to the government, but they in turn allowed its assignment to other ongoing research within the institution on completion of a project, so that none was returned or auctioned. Government welfare funds to support indigent patient care posed no problem for the hospital, as they were interpreted for definite and full services rendered.

Early Years Under President Harold W. Tribble

The first year of this decade was highlighted by the onset of the Korean War in June 1950 and the reactivation of Selective Service. Medical students were deferred and no faculty members were called to service at the outset. In September 1950 Dr. Harold W. Tribble replaced Dr. Thurman Kitchin as president of Wake Forest College. Tribble, a Baptist with a strong scholarly and theologic background, came from the presidency of Andover-Newton Theological School in Massachusetts. His first priority was to complete the college fund-raising campaign and, with the architect selected previously by the trustees, to plan the new Reynolda campus in Winston-Salem. He had little time to oversee the academic program of the college, which he delegated to Dean D.B. Bryan. The president employed Mr. Robert G. Deyton as vice president and controller and gave him the responsibility for business and financial affairs of the entire college. As will be seen, this initiated a very tense relationship between the medical school and administration of the college concerning financial planning and utilization of medical service income.

The medical school had received a contribution of $50,000 from Mr. Charles L. Amos, Sr. of High Point in December 1950 for the construction of a building at the Graylyn estate for the care and treatment of geriatric patients. It became known as Amos Cottage. At the same time, 26 beds were added to the manor house, bringing the total beds in this neuropsychiatric facility to 60. At the request of Dr. Tribble, he, Mr. Deyton and their staff used Amos Cottage for local administrative offices until the college moved to Winston-Salem in June 1956. Thereafter, Amos Cottage was used as a facility for retarded children under the direction of Dr. Alanson Hinman of the Department of Pediatrics.

Also during the early part of the 1950s several important changes occurred at the medical school. During 1951 Dr. Frank R. Lock was appointed associate dean and medical director of the hospital, the latter title having been held by Dean Carpenter since the beginning of the four-year school. The hospital trustees, by resolution, designated that the medical and surgical staff would be limited to the faculty of the medical school. This had been an earlier stated policy, but was not fully activated until this action by the hospital trustees.

Dr. George T. Harrell, chairman of medicine, requested that he be given more time for his research and became research professor of medicine in July 1952. Dr. Ernest H. Yount, a member of the Department of Medicine, a graduate of Vanderbilt University and a Markle Scholar, was appointed chairman of that department. One year later Dr. Harrell accepted the deanship of the new University of Florida School of Medicine, and later planned and was responsible for the construction of a second new school, the Pennsylvania State University School of Medicine.

The medical school continued under borderline finances. Since 1947 budgets were submitted each year to the trustees and approved with the proviso that the dean raise the amount of the deficit or decrease spending. In 1951 Graylyn showed its first loss which was attributed to part-pay patients, census problems due to a decrease in the average length of stay and a shift to ambulatory treatment allowed by thorazine and its successor drug therapies. Fortunately, the debt on the original medical school building was being amortized through the income from the James A. Gray Trust that initially was restricted for this purpose. The final payment on the note was made in 1955 through a contribution of $10,000 from the college.

Other changes in administration occurred during the early 1950s. Dr. Thomas T. Mackie was released from duties in July 1951 and the Institute of Tropical Medicine was phased out. Dr. Manson Meads, a member of the Department of Medicine since 1947, was appointed director of the Department of Preventive Medicine and was joined in the department by Drs. Lucile W. Hutaff and C. Nash Herndon. Also, in that year the faculty mourned the deaths of Dr. Herbert M. Vann, a long-time faculty member who had made outstanding contributions to the school; and Mr. William Neal Reynolds at the age of 88, a generous benefactor of Baptist Hospital and Wake Forest College. Mr. James A. Gray died on October 29, 1952, at the age of 63, and the school lost a key advisor, philanthropist and community leader who had contributed much to the origin and early development of the four-year institution.

The first funded professorship was established at the medical school in 1953 in medical genetics. It was established by a New York philanthropist with a deep interest in population genetics who made a gift of stock valued at $100,000. The donor had been supporting for several years the research of Dr. C. Nash Herndon on the genetic effects of intermarriage in Watauga County, North Carolina. The conditions of the professorship were that the donor remain anonymous, that the professorship be given to Dr. Herndon or his successor, and the funds be invested and amortized completely over a thirty-year period for the benefit of the recipient and his research.

In February 1953 Dr. Carpenter was granted a leave of absence for one year, beginning July 1, to serve as Fulbright Visiting Professor at the University of Cairo. Dr. Wingate M. Johnson served as acting dean during this period. A medical school committee had been appointed by the Faculty Executive Council to explore obtaining additional space for the school, with Mr. Clyde Hardy serving as chairman. Dr. Tribble requested that the committee deal directly with Mr. Deyton, "as he knows my feeling." Mr. Deyton met with the committee, indicated that he was making a thorough study of the organization of the school with particular attention to the Private Diagnostic Clinic, and requested specific information on the professional income of individual faculty members. A crisis arose when word of this reached the faculty. It must be remembered that up to this time the school had been separated by 110 miles from the college and its central administration and basically had been left to its own devices in terms of organization and financing. Also, the cost of building the new campus was rising rapidly.

Dr. Tribble and Mr. Deyton met with the entire faculty on April 1, 1953, and the president proposed that professional income from patient care might be used to solve the problems of the operating budget and over-crowded facilities "without adding to the financial burden of the college in its transition period to the new campus." Further, he stated he wanted a study of the entire matter. Discussion was lively and, at times, heated. In the end, the faculty remained highly suspicious of the president's underlying motivations. On the initiative of the acting dean and the faculty, the trustees appointed a special committee in June 1953 to assist in clarifying the policies of the medical school. This committee was directed to study the "total field of operations of the medical school." The trustees also adopted a resolution at that time that "all budgets of Wake Forest College shall be operated by the vice president and controller . . . provided the dean of the Medical School shall be responsible for the operation of the school within the total budget adopted by the Trustees." This important policy, arising out of controversy, recognized that medical schools differ from other schools within a university in their mechanisms of financing. It allowed flexibility in day-to-day budget management, and properly placed responsibility and accountability with the dean.

The Committee on the Medical School consisted of Mr. Basil Watkins, chairman, Mr. O.M. Mull, Dr. Claude U. Broach, Dr. E.H. Herring, Dr. John Hamrick and Dr. W.A. Hoover. After considerable delay they met in earnest in 1954 and focused on the Private Diagnostic Clinic and administrative relations between the school and college. Dr. Tribble continued to promote some voluntary plan to utilize PDC income to meet medical school needs. Faculty morale was at a low ebb due to insecurity about the future. Finally, the trustee committee requested that a medical school committee, made up of representatives of the Faculty Executive Council and the Private Diagnostic Clinic, develop a proposal for policies for the operation of the school and the PDC and for the construction of a new building for the medical school. A five-page statement was submitted, modified somewhat by the trustee committee, and approved by the full board on October 1, 1954. This became known as "Appendix B," an official part of the bylaws of the college. In essence, it stated the fundamental activities of the school, affirmed its quest for excellence, and noted the importance of maintaining a proper balance between teaching, research and patient care. It spoke to faculty and student selection, the duties of the dean and his relation to the college administration and trustees, finances, and faculty compensation and professional earnings. The policy on budget mentioned above was reaffirmed.

To remove from the minds of the faculty the threat of financial insecurity, the policy statement assured that "the present plan of financial operation will continue as established policy." One policy statement (though it still remains a part of the bylaws) was never implemented. It stated the "Board of Trustees of Wake Forest College will appropriate to the Medical School each budget year an equitable share of the income from the general endowment of the College and from the Baptist State Convention of North Carolina." However, one year later the trustees did increase the annual appropriation to the medical school from general funds from $37,450 to $50,000. It continues at this level. During its entire history the school received no funds from the Baptist convention either directly or through the college. The special committee recognized that more planning was needed for the proposed addition to the medical school and made no specific recommendations on the matter.

Several additional administrative changes were made during this time. In August 1954 Dr. Robert B. Lawson, who had served on the faculty since 1942 and very ably as director of the Department of Pediatrics since 1950, resigned to accept a similar position at the University of Miami School of Medicine. Dr. Weston M. Kelsey, a senior member of the department, succeeded him. The Department of Radiology, which had been unsettled by several changes in leadership, was greatly strengthened in August 1955 by the appointment of Dr. Isadore Meschan from the University of Arkansas School of Medicine as director. Dr. Robert L. Tuttle returned from military service in December 1954, becoming director of the Department of Bacteriology and Immunology, replacing his wife Dorothy who had served as director since July 1953.

One underlying theme that surfaced during the study of the special committee on the medical school was the increasing demands that were being placed on the deanship. This was clearly recognized by Dr. Carpenter who, because of fiscal circumstances, received most of his compensation from medical service income generated by the Department of Pathology. Nationally, a trend toward full-time deans was evident. The Deitrick and Berson study in 1950 revealed that of the 36 private medical schools, 20 deans received their entire salary from the deanship and the remainder had mixed sources of income from departmental duties and/or consultation fees[2]. The medical school faculty requested that Dr. Carpenter continue as dean and an active member of the Department of Pathology, and urged him to add part-time support at the central administrative level. As such, when Dr. Manson Meads returned from two years of service with the Public Health Service in Thailand in October 1955, he was asked to serve as associate dean responsible for academic and scientific programs. Initially, this was a part-time assignment, in addition to his duties as director of the Department of Preventive Medicine, which had been well carried out by Dr. Lucile Hutaff as acting director in his absence. Dr. Carpenter requested that Dr. Meads also give special emphasis to planning for the future development of the school.

A Tumultuous Five Years (1956–1960)

Wake Forest moved to its new Reynolda campus in Winston-Salem during a four-week period that culminated with the opening of the summer session on June 18, 1956. The cost of the new campus, estimated at $6 million in 1950, had risen to $19.5 million by that time. Many said this would be the last private college to move en masse to a new location. It was a remarkable achievement, and primarily the result of the singular purpose and tenacity of President Tribble, and the foresight and generosity of the Reynolds family and associated foundations who recognized the valuable contributions that a respected institution of higher education could make to the community and region. In his historical account, Coy Carpenter relates his own role in bringing the idea of the move to fruition, and notes that the benefactors also believed that the prestige of the medical school would be enhanced by a stronger Wake Forest. Subsequent history clearly demonstrates the mutual benefits of this momentous event.

The move came two years after the completion of the South Wing of Baptist Hospital. The institution was financially stable, admissions exceeded 15,000, and over 120,000 patient visits were recorded to the Outpatient Department and Private Diagnostic Clinic. The older hospital buildings had been air-conditioned through grants from the Duke Endowment and Ford Foundation. A cobalt-60 radiation therapy unit was under construction and became operational in May 1956.

It was the first such installation in North Carolina. The Davis Memorial Chapel was nearing completion. This major landmark at the medical center was given by the Atlas Supply Company, owned by the E.L. Davis family, as a memorial to Mrs. Annie Pearl Shore Davis and in honor of Mr. Egbert L. Davis, Sr. The beautiful structure is located adjacent to the hospital and medical school and serves patients, families, staff and students who seek a quiet visit or wish to take part in group worship.

During 1956, the educational role of the Baptist Hospital had expanded. It boasted the largest diploma school of nursing in the state with a student body of 175. It maintained separate schools for medical technologists, cytotechnologists, x-ray technologists, nurse anesthetists, medical record librarians, practical nurses and pastoral counselors. The hospital served also as the clinical training site of 70 interns and residents and 120 third- and fourth-year medical students.

Unlike the progress being made by Baptist Hospital, the beginning of this period for the medical school was still grim. The dean reported to the trustees that the "educational and general budget proposed for 1956–1957 was the lowest of any four-year private school except for the two negro institutions."[3] The additional beds of the south wing had enhanced professional income and clinical faculty development, but the continued severe limitations of space and other income prevented development of the basic medical sciences, the graduate program and research. Despite these circumstances, many of the faculty continued to believe in the future of the school, seeing problems as challenges to be overcome. For example, Dr. William Boyce, a brilliant young urologist, pitched an army surplus tent on the roof of the medical school when additional space was required for his advanced research on kidney stone formation.

In addition to the move of Wake Forest College, several other important events occurred during the last half of this decade, which prefaced a period of major growth of the center. These involved the solution of the issue of church-state and federal grants, the initiation of an innovative process for planning and evaluation, a catalyzing accreditation survey and the reorganization of the Private Diagnostic Clinic as an integral part of the school of medicine. Each will be described separately.

Church-State Issue Resolved; Medical School Enlarged

With the move of the college completed, the medical school was freed to seek funds to resolve its critical shortage of space. Initially a five-floor addition was planned that would approximately double the size of the institution. Mr. P. Huber Hanes, chairman of the board of the P.H. Hanes Knitting Company, agreed to head a $1-million fund-raising campaign to finance the project. A total of $1,187,946 was received during November and December 1956, with major contributions of $410,000 from the R.J. Reynolds Tobacco Company and $250,000 from the Z. Smith Reynolds Foundation. At the same time the Health Research Facilities Act became law, through which matching grants for research facilities construction were available to non-federal institutions. Major authorizations by Congress for this and other research and development programs undoubtedly were stimulated by the Russian success with Sputnik I in 1957, an event that Lyndon Johnson termed a "technological Pearl Harbor."

One might surmise also that the broad public reaction to this technologic achievement by the Russians resulted in the more flexible view of the Baptist State Convention of North Carolina toward federal aid for research. With the cautious encouragement of the college trustees, the medical school expanded its building plans and applied for a matching federal grant to finance the portions of the facility designated for research activities. Clyde T. Hardy, Jr. served as coordinator between the medical school and architect, one of his many contributions in a liaison capacity within the medical center. During this process, Coy Carpenter was discussing the matter with Baptist leaders. At a crucial meeting in High Point, the Reverend Casper Warren, then president of the Baptist State Convention, asked emotionally, "How can we prevent the medical school from receiving federal funds when we [the convention] have never given them one nickle?"[4] As a result of this key meeting, the convention Committee of Twenty-five was asked to reconsider the whole area of federal grants-in-aid, report its recommendations to the General Board and finally to the convention at the annual meeting in November 1957.

It is recorded that this annual session of the convention, held in Raleigh, November 19–21, was attended by the largest number of Baptists in convention history, and was "a rather turbulent" affair. The issue on the agenda that had stimulated major interest was the question of approving social dancing on the campuses of Baptist colleges. Although dancing on campus seems trivial today, it was sufficiently newsworthy in 1957 to be given space in *Life* magazine. The report of the Committee of Twenty-five was brief and recommended that the convention approve the facilities grant "as we have other research grants that have been our practice in the past."[5] The report was approved by the convention with little discussion and no dissent. Not so the dancing issue, which was hotly debated and overwhelmingly disapproved. To this day, some cynics hold that it was the medical school that conjured up the dancing issue in order to divert attention from the question of acceptance of federal aid by the Baptist institutions and agencies. The following requirements were mandated.[6]

1. The convention shall require its agencies and institutions to present any programs for government grants or any form of government aid not already authorized in kind by convention action to the general board of the convention for review before agreements are made.

2. Acceptance of such grants or aid shall be based upon approval of both trustees of the institution or agency involved and the general board.

3. All institutions or agencies operating in cooperation with government as above shall report annually upon such operations to the convention through its general board.

As an aftermath, the medical school promptly requested and received approval for all categories of federal grant programs available, i.e., fellowships, undergraduate and graduate training grants, etc. All were noted as being free from government interference and control and consistent with the policy of services rendered. As such, this major issue was resolved for the school of medicine.

Historically, it is of interest that Baylor University, the only other Baptist institution that had a medical school at the time, resolved the issue of federal funds in an entirely different manner. An independent medical foundation was established by the school through which faculty members applied for and received federal grants. Further, when the foundation received federal grants for construction, it held title to the facilities and leased them to the medical school for one dollar a year. In 1969 this mechanism no longer became necessary when the Baylor trustees divested the medical school making it a free-standing institution with an independent governance.

Bowman Gray had the advantage over many schools at this time in early receipt of Health Research Facilities grants, as the necessary matching funds were in hand as a result of the 1956 campaign. Five successive federal grants were approved between 1957 and 1959 totaling $1,092,045, which allowed for the completion of the building that was planned initially, and named for the late James A. Gray, and also for the Research Center Building, a greatly expanded and modern vivarium and a five-floor addition above that facility.

A total of 122,000 square feet was added during this period at a cost of $2,179,627. A special alumni campaign, headed by Dr. George W. Paschal, Jr., raised $571,804 to help complete the program. These facilities and associated renovations not only provided space for additional faculty and research, but also for supporting staff and services, library and classroom expansion, and a student lounge.

Administrative Changes

In January 1957 it was possible to increase administrative support in order to meet the needs of students and faculty more effectively and to give needed time to planning for the expansion of facilities, the strengthening of academic programs and fund-raising. Dr. Carpenter, as dean, focused his efforts on external affairs, Graylyn and overall policy and development. Dr. Meads, as associate dean, devoted almost full time to internal affairs and planning. Dr. C. Nash Herndon was appointed chairman of the Department of Preventive Medicine. Dr. Meads was assisted by Dr. J. Maxwell Little as part-time assistant dean for admissions and student evaluation. Mr. Harry O. Parker, as controller, was responsible for buildings and grounds, grants management, and overall budget in cooperation with the dean and associate dean. Dr. Lock had relinquished the position of medical director to devote more time to his department and a major research project on the impact of rubella on pregnancy. The position of medical director was renamed Chief of Professional Services. Dr. Eben Alexander, head of the Section of Neurosurgery, was elected to that position. He modestly claims this was because his name began with "A," but he carried out his responsibility with such integrity, fairness and leadership that he was reelected to this position annually for a period of twenty years.

A star was born with the appointment of Thomas B. Clarkson, Jr., D.V.M., as director of the Vivarium in 1957. He had graduated from the University of Georgia School of Veterinary Medicine in 1954, following which he served as a research associate at S. E. Massengill

Company, Bristol, Tennessee. Clarkson quickly elevated the standards of animal care and research, participated in the design of the new vivarium facilities and the development of an animal research farm. As will be seen, he made major contributions to the training of academic veterinarians for other medical schools and through his broad-based research in atherosclerosis.

Planning for the Future — An Experiment in Faculty Self-evaluation

A comprehensive study of the past history and present status of the medical school was initiated in 1957. It included a review of stated aims, objectives, policies and organization; the collection of objective data on finances, faculty growth, facilities and programs; and an analysis of the time the faculty members spent in teaching, research, patient care and administration. A small committee was then appointed to review the information and make recommendations for the future. The committee consisted of William H. Boyce (Surgery), Clyde T. Hardy, Jr. (Private Diagnostic Clinic administrator), C. Nash Herndon (Preventive Medicine), J. Maxwell Little (Pharmacology), Ernest H. Yount, Jr. (Medicine), with Dr. Meads serving as chairman. From the outset it was decided that major attention should be focused on the ecology of the faculty, that is, the identification and analysis of all factors in the medical school environment which affect academic development and achievement of the faculty as individuals and as a group. The committee held 20 meetings and prepared a 93-page report that included the basic information on past history and present status of the institution, a summary of committee discussions and recommendations, and an outline of policy guidelines for the future development of the school.[7]

The report was distributed to the faculty ten days before a retreat held in Roanoke, Virginia June 5-7, 1958. Ninety percent of the full-time faculty attended. The college president and the dean of arts and sciences, the administrator of the North Carolina Baptist Hospital and Dr. Stanley Olson, then dean of Baylor Medical School, were present as consultants. Though the retreat or workshop approach had been used for some time by industry and government, to our knowledge this was its first adaptation to a medical school in this country. In recognition of this, the National Fund for Medical Education made a grant to the school to help defray expenses. We were grateful for the contributions made by Dr. Robert W. Prichard, who served as retreat manager, and to members of the part-time faculty who covered some of the essential duties at the medical center during the three-day period. An assessment of the self-study was reported to the 69th annual meeting of the Association of American Medical Colleges.[8] In summary, it was the unanimous opinion of the participants that this experiment in critical self-analysis was a valuable and much needed reorientation for everyone; it exposed drifts and trends, both good and bad, within the institution, and formed the basis for sound planning for the future direction of the center. Some years later institutional self-studies became a mandatory part of the accreditation process for all medical schools.

There was little doubt that this experiment created a healthy ferment among the faculty, and steps were taken to put certain conference recommendations into effect immediately. Others were translated into specific plans or policies to be implemented according to priority as resources permitted. These plans included correction of excessive academic loads in certain departments, expansion of the basic medical sciences, graduate education and fundamental research and a library adequate to support these activities. Also indicated were improvements in clinical facilities, an increase in student scholarship and loan funds, better methods for student selection and evaluation, curriculum improvement, stronger academic affiliation with Wake Forest College, development of better methods for determining the extent and costs of the various institutional functions, and improvement in public and alumni relations. The study committee decided not to meet again as a group to avoid any implication that they had become a "kitchen cabinet." Academic policy had been clearly defined as a responsibility of the faculty as a whole, as had their important role in long-range planning.

The institution was able to move forward in several areas of high priority during the next several years due to expanded facilities, an increase in the number of federal research and training grants, and several timely gifts from the private sector.

During the mid-1950s the Ford Foundation had developed a serious concern for the financial stability of private medical schools in this country. In 1956 it distributed $90 million by formula among these 45 accredited institutions. Recipients were to use the funds as temporary endowment for ten years for purposes other than research or construction. Bowman Gray received $1.6 million and all income from this source was used to improve salaries of faculty in the basic medical sciences. After the required 10-year period a number of schools liquidated the core grant for construction or other purposes. In keeping with its prudent fiscal policy, Bowman Gray has maintained these funds as part of its permanent endowment, which now have a value of $3,436,041.

The Z. Smith Reynolds Foundation established a major scholarship program at the medical school in 1957 at the suggestion of Mr. Richard J. Reynolds, Jr. Its purpose was to encourage bright young North Carolinians to study medicine, free them of financial concerns through liberal support, and encourage them to remain in the state to practice after the completion of their training. The school received $150,000 annually to support eight Reynolds scholars per year for four years of medical school; further assistance was provided during their internship period. The program is described in more detail in Dr. Carpenter's history and, needless to say, it made a major impact on the quality of the student body and the image of the institution. During the 15 years that the scholarships were available, 121 students received this financial support. It is of interest that a significantly higher percentage of these students (18%) chose academic careers in medicine than our graduates as a whole during this time. A survey of Reynolds scholars in 1984 indicated that 65% were still in practice or in academic positions in North Carolina.

Several other generous gifts received during this period were directed at areas of high-priority needs. In 1959 Mrs. Anne Cannon Reynolds Tate and Mrs. Nathalie Gray Bernard gave $250,000 each to establish named professorships in anatomy, biochemistry, and physiology. Again, in 1960, Mrs. Tate gave the school 9,000 shares of R.J. Reynolds stock which was added to the endowment. In the early 1960s gifts of $125,000 from the R.J. Reynolds Tobacco Company and $75,000 from the Z. Smith Reynolds Foundation met a critical need for correcting deficits in library back files. Also during this time Bowman and Gordon Gray established living trusts for the school, to which they contributed periodically during their lifetimes.

A Catalytic Accreditation Survey

A Liaison Committee survey team representing the American Medical Association and the Association of American Medical Colleges visited the medical school during January 1959. Although the school had been included in the Deitrick-Berson study of medical schools at mid-century, the last official visit on behalf of these organizations had been 16 years earlier, in October 1943. The visitors pointed out numerous problems related to organization, financing, faculty, the Private Diagnostic Clinic, curriculum and library. However, they recognized high faculty morale, recently expanded facilities and that the school, through a comprehensive self-study, was "seeking constructive resolution of its various challenges." They reported that the school was obviously in a stage of transition and recommended full approval with a revisit within three to four years, rather than the usual seven.

The immediate reaction to this visit was traumatic to say the least; however, in retrospect, it was an historical milestone that served as a powerful catalyst to move forward as quickly as possible with the further implementation of guidelines and priorities established by the faculty at the Roanoke retreat.

In the area of finances, the school had been criticized for a laissez-faire approach to faculty private practice, for the autonomy of the Private Diagnostic Clinic within the institution, for excluding medical service income from the budget (which gave an erroneous impression of total funds actually involved in operations), and also for the limited support of the basic medical sciences. A committee of the faculty, chaired by Dr. Howard H. Bradshaw, endorsed the implementation of "composite budgeting" under which departments involved in clinical practice were required to develop a plan for group endeavor and to present budget requests that included all sources of income. In developing the group endeavor proposals, it was acceptable for medical service income to be used to supplement salaries from other sources to achieve a functional balance among teaching, research, and specialty representation in patient care within each department. Individual income of faculty members from medical service continued to be limited by time, available hospital beds and the acceptable performance of academic responsibilities. All agreed that the establishment of income ceilings would severely dampen incentives which could reduce the quality of patient care and the important function of faculty as role models for students and house staff. The committee recommended further that the Private Diagnostic Clinic become a service department of the medical school with the business manager responsible directly to the dean. The name was changed to the Department of Clinics (DOC) and a committee of clinical faculty was established to advise the administration on operations and management. To assist in strengthening the basic medical sciences the clinical departments agreed to a reallocation of a major part of basic school dollars in their budgets for this purpose.

These major recommendations of the Bradshaw committee were discussed at length with and among the clinical faculty, and were not without dissent. However, in the end only three of the 58 clinical faculty involved decided to leave the institution when the recommendations were implemented. Much credit for this nearly unanimous decision is due to the leadership of the clinical department chairmen, the supportive liaison role of Clyde T. Hardy, Jr., and the ultimate concurrence of the president and college trustees. It represented again the remarkable response of the clinical faculty to a crisis situation by making the best interests of the total institution the first priority, a hallmark that has persisted throughout the history of the medical school.

Several other major studies were initiated after the accreditation survey that included a comprehensive review of the curriculum, ways and means to strengthen the basic medical sciences to allow the development of Ph.D. programs and, finally, a complete review of organization and the codification of policies that had evolved from the institutional self-study of 1957–1958. Each will be described briefly.

With the exception of the addition of a fourth quarter to the junior year in 1958, little change had been made in the overall curriculum during past years. The objectives of the comprehensive study by the Committee on Medical Education under the chairmanship of Dr. Charles L. Spurr, initiated in 1959, were to increase the graduate orientation of the program, introduce free and elective time, reduce an excessive lecture schedule, improve the correlation between the basic medical sciences which was handicapped by block teaching, and allow students more time for the individual study of patients. These objectives were accomplished to a large degree during the ensuing four years and culminated in another faculty retreat where final consensus on several segments of the study was accomplished.

The key elements needed to strengthen and expand the basic medical sciences were space, financial support, upgrading of the library and the establishment of a credible graduate program leading to Ph.D. degree. The last was critical if the institution was to attract high quality faculty in the fields of anatomy, biochemistry, physiology, pharmacology and microbiology. The new facilities that were under construction provided the space. New income from internal sources, previously mentioned private gifts, and federal training and fellowship grants provided support for new faculty and for upgrading the library collection and staff. Expansion of the graduate program posed a problem in initial discussions with representatives from the college, who indicated that their priority was on the improvement of the liberal arts program; this meant delaying action on graduate education. It appeared that the only option for the medical school was to add needed support in physics, biology and chemistry to its own faculty, similar to the pattern that had been used by the Massachusetts Institute of Technology. Fortunately, when President Tribble heard of this plan, he insisted that graduate education should develop as a total college function, and an institution-wide committee was established to make recommendations toward this end. The pressure from the medical school broke the ice and accelerated plans for graduate education at Wake Forest. The first step was the development of the graduate school, and initial emphasis was given to the natural sciences with the reactivation of the M.S. degree program at the college. Dr. Richard L. Burt, associate professor of Obstetrics and Gynecology, who had a Ph.D. in microbiology in addition to an M.D. degree, was given the responsibility for developing the graduate program at the medical school, in coordination with essential departments on the Reynolda campus. This resulted in the successive development of Ph.D. programs in Anatomy (1961), Physiology and Pharmacology (1962), Biochemistry (1963) and Microbiology (1964). Critical to this development were the appointments of new chairmen in three of these departments—Dr. Norman M. Sulkin (Anatomy), Dr. Cornelius Strittmatter (Biochemistry) and Dr. Quentin Myrvik (Microbiology). Their presence, and the faculty they recruited, brought in additional federal grants for research, research training, and fellowships that increased significantly the total resources available for both the graduate and medical education programs.

Shortly after the first Roanoke retreat in 1958, the central administration was reorganized for the purpose of implementing the major recommendations of that conference. Dr. Carpenter changed his title to executive dean and focused on external affairs, including Graylyn and fund raising. He asked Dr. Meads to serve as academic dean with the responsibility for internal affairs, including the chairing of the Faculty Executive Council. Some confusion arose during the ensuing year because certain areas of responsibility and authority had not been clearly defined. Following a study of the matter by a committee of department chairmen in September 1959, Dr. Carpenter again took the title of dean and Dr. Meads was made executive dean, with responsibility for internal affairs and the authority to act in financial, organizational and other matters. Within the context of the faculty self-evaluation study and aided by valuable advice given Dr. Meads by senior medical school administrators such as Dr. Vernon Lippard (Yale), Maxwell Lapham (Tulane), Lowell Coggeshall (Chicago) and John Deitrick (Cornell), the responsibility and authority of the faculty, department chairmen and section heads, and central administration were clarified and comprehensive policies concerning faculty members were codified. During this time the department chairmen became the Faculty Executive Council with the responsibility for policies related to academic programs, students and faculty. These functions were supported by the central administration, faculty committees, and through the establishment of a faculty forum for discussion of academic policy matters by the entire faculty. The option of a faculty forum was chosen by the executive council rather than establishing a medical school faculty senate with parliamentary functions. It was determined that support for the areas of student affairs and professional services could be fully delegated to an assistant dean and the chief of professional services, respectively, with the executive dean maintaining responsibility for budget, committee appointments, space assignment, service departments and internal planning.

This was a time in which the growth of scientific knowledge was accelerating rapidly. Specialization, and the traditional patterns of medical school organization, were beginning to inhibit effective coordination of effort in many developing fields of interest that cut across departmental lines. Pressures were developing also for the elevation of subspecialties to the level of full departments, but many believed this would lead to further fragmentation and an increase in the costs and complexity of administration. Formal intramural institutes or centers were established in some medical schools to focus on and enhance research in multidisciplinary areas such as cancer and heart disease. The Faculty Executive Council at this time wisely chose instead to follow the lead of Yale and approved the formation of multidisciplinary study groups within the framework of the existing institutional organization. Their purpose was to promote cooperation, coordination and the stimulation of interest among faculty members with common purposes. The initiative to form such a group was to originate from within the faculty, and the group was to define its purpose, elect a coordinator and become established with the approval of the Faculty Executive Council. These groups, by policy, could not be assigned specially designated space or budget; such elements remained within departments. During the ensuing year, multidisciplinary groups were designated in the neurosciences, atherosclerosis, oncology, cell biology and renal disease. They served effectively to enhance research and teaching, and later aided significantly in attracting outside financial support to these fields.

Developments in Patient Care

Beginning in 1941, the clinical laboratory services for the center were owned by the medical school and operated by the Department of Pathology. The hospital collected payment from patients and reimbursed the medical school for services rendered in an amount agreed upon annually as adequate for proper staffing, equipment, and other basic operating expenses. These yearly negotiations grew increasingly difficult in the early 1950s. The problem came to a head in 1956 when the increase in the budget requested by the medical school was denied despite the fact that laboratory revenue to the hospital had been increasing at a far greater rate than payment by the hospital to the school. This frustrating problem was resolved when, on the recommendation of the dean, the trustees of the college and hospital agreed to a transfer of space and equipment (appraised value of $265,000) to the hospital for the sum of $25,000.[9] The hospital then delegated responsibility for the operation of the clinical laboratories to the Department of Pathology under an agreement to reimburse the full costs of operation. Dr. Robert W. Prichard, on his return from a two-year tour of duty with the U. S. Public Health Service in Thailand in 1957, was named director of clinical laboratories and with unusual tact and diplomacy elevated and maintained the standards of the laboratories to a level comparable with the best institutions in the country. The laboratories, in turn, became an important profit center for the hospital.

Despite the addition of the South Wing in 1954, pressures increased for more hospital beds and for the expansion of the student body of the school of nursing. Reid Holmes found that a number of convalescent patients from out of the county could be moved from acute care beds to a self-care facility if available, or could have been admitted to such a facility for diagnostic studies or limited treatment.

His intent was to make available more acute care beds while significantly lowering costs to such patients. The professional staff agreed with the plan and in a far-sighted move in 1959 the hospital purchased Twin Castles Apartments from Mr. George Kempton at a cost of $850,000.[10] Twin Castles, built in 1939, consisted of several two-story, brick, fireproof buildings containing 127 apartments on 7 acres of land directly adjacent to hospital property. An expanded nursing student body was housed in 75 apartments and other units were rented to medical center personnel. At the same time the old nurses home was converted to 79 hotel-type patient rooms with a single nursing station. This unit, known as the Progressive Care Center (PCC), opened in March 1961. Pledges totaling $485,000 had been made by the Duke Endowment, the Mary Reynolds Babcock Foundation and R.J. Reynolds Tobacco Company for these projects, and the remainder was financed through borrowed funds and amortized through an initial room charge of $10 per day. Through the persistence of Mr. Holmes, these beds were licensed by the state and then qualified by health insurance companies for reimbursement. This unit raised the total bed capacity of Baptist Hospital to 499, plus 50 bassinets. The PCC, the first in the southeast, received national attention. It long served as a model for other institutions. However, in the absence of personal financial incentives, it was found difficult to move convalescing patients, who had insurance coverage, to this unit for the several days before discharge. As such, the PCC served primarily out-of-town patients who were ambulatory and required diagnostic studies and/or limited treatment, but who did not need close nursing supervision.

Recurring shortages of hospital beds also existed in Winston-Salem's City Hospital. One hundred beds had been added in 1950 and a few years later a citizens committee, chaired by Mr. James G. Hanes, was appointed to study further hospital needs. In November 1957 the committee recommended the construction of a new 550-570 bed hospital and modernization of the City Hospital to replace the Kate Bitting Reynolds Hospital.[11] During the discussions it was proposed that the new City Hospital be located adjacent to Baptist Hospital and, with the Kate Bitting Reynolds Hospital, the three be joined under an umbrella organization called Forsyth Medical Center. Under the plan, separate governances would be maintained, but close cooperation would be fostered to strengthen educational programs, to improve the care of indigent patients and to eliminate unnecessary duplication of services. Though supported by the Bowman Gray-Baptist Hospital Medical Center, objections to the plan by the staff of City Hospital prevailed. Under the leadership of Mr. John Whitaker, a bond issue was passed in 1959 and the 550-bed Forsyth Memorial Hospital was constructed on a 77-acre tract in the western part of the city. It opened in April 1964. Remodeling of the old City Hospital building was abandoned and the county instead built a new 250-bed Reynolds Memorial Hospital in east Winston near the old unit that was opened in January 1970.

Graylyn, as a neuropsychiatric unit, again developed problems of low occupancy and increasing deficits and was closed as a hospital unit in January 1959. Inpatient psychiatry was consolidated at Baptist Hospital. The Graylyn hospital facility was offered to the North Carolina Baptist Hospital for $1 per year to operate as a supplemental psychiatric unit but the offer was not accepted. Graylyn continued, however, as a "children's center" housing the medical school-affiliated Child Guidance Clinic and Center for Handicapped Children. The medical school itself operated Amos Cottage for retarded children and an enlarged psychology, reading and speech clinic. The latter was a cooperative program with the city and county school system, funded initially by a five-year $338,250 grant from the Mary Reynolds Babcock Foundation.

The Department of Psychiatry and Neurology had undergone changes during this time. Dr. Lloyd J. Thompson resigned as department chairman in 1956, and Dr. Angus Randolph was appointed acting chairman, serving until June 1960, when Dr. Richard C. Proctor agreed to assume the chairmanship. This was a time in which psychoanalysis dominated psychiatry and, as such, was causing problems of proper balance in many medical schools. Dr. Proctor, a Bowman Gray graduate, was trained as an eclectic psychiatrist and was chosen to develop the educational and patient care programs with that orientation.

The discipline of neurology, through the stimulus of research training and fellowship grants from the National Institute of Neurologic Diseases and Blindness, was evolving rapidly as a legitimate field in its own right. In 1957 Dr. Richard L. Masland, head of the Section of Neurology who had served for ten years as a valuable and nationally recognized neurologist on the faculty, left to become assistant director of the National Institute. In keeping with the rapid evolution of neurology, a separate department was formed at the

James A. Gray

Nathalie Gray Bernard

Bowman Gray, Jr.

Gordon Gray

Coy C. Carpenter, M.D.

Wingate M. Johnson, M.D.

Ray E. Brown

Odus M. Mull

P. Huber Hanes, Sr.

Original Medical Center Facilities
Winston–Salem (1946)

Graylyn

Amphitheater

Front Entrance to Original Four-year Medical School
Winston-Salem

Reid T. Holmes

Harold W. Tribble

North Carolina Baptist Hospital-Davis Chapel

medical school in 1960. Dr. Martin Netsky, a Bowman Gray neuropathologist with board certifications also in neurology and psychiatry, was appointed chairman. Emphasis was given to the academic aspects of this discipline. In 1962 Dr. Netsky returned to full-time neuropathology by accepting an appointment at the University of Virginia; and Dr. James F. Toole from the University of Pennsylvania was elected to the chairmanship. Toole represented the "new guard" with board certification in both internal medicine and neurology. As will be noted later, through his creative leadership over a period of 20 years, neurology at the center has become nationally recognized and many contributions to the advancement of this field were made, particularly in the area of cerebrovascular disease and sonography. Pioneering studies in the latter area led to the establishment of the internationally recognized postgraduate multidisciplinary training program in medical ultrasound, developed by Drs. James Martin and William McKinney.

References and Notes

1. Deitrick, John E. and Berson, Robert C., Medical Schools in the United States at Mid-Century. McGraw-Hill Book Co., New York, 1953.
2. *Ibid.*
3. The official budget of the medical school at that time did not include medical service income.
4. Personal observation
5. Annual of the Baptist State Convention of North Carolina 1957, pp. 55–57.
6. Annual of the Baptist State Convention of North Carolina 1958, pp. 78–81.
7. Report of Medical School Study Committee, May 1958.
8. Study Committee, "Experiment in Faculty Self-evaluation," J. Med Ed. 35:175–77, (Feb. 1960).
9. Agreement date September 24, 1957 (That is the date of the Wake Forest University Trustee meeting and the date of the Trustee lease agreement resolution).
10. Annual of the Baptist State Convention of North Carolina 1959, pp. 202–204; and 1970, p. 163.
11. Prichard, Robert W. Medicine, Vol. 11, Winston-Salem in History, published by Historic Winston, 1976.

CHAPTER V

The Transitional Years—
Meeting Social Needs
in the 1960s

At the beginning of 1960 the country was on the verge of a revolution in social policy. Since World War II national health policy had focused on expansion of the hospital system through the Hill-Burton legislation and on biomedical research, mainly through the National Institutes of Health. As a result, there had been a proliferation of small rural hospitals, expansion of existing urban hospitals, and a rapid increase in scientific knowledge and technology. Specialization in medicine increased, and public expectations for medicine were greatly enhanced. The number and variety of allied health personnel multiplied. These factors, and an expanding private health insurance system, increased sharply the demand for medical care.

Warnings of a developing shortage of physicians was voiced in the early 1950s by the Association of American Medical Colleges, which called for an expansion of existing schools and the development of new ones in universities located in major population centers. However, the association emphasized that this could not be accomplished without first strengthening medical school finances. The Commonwealth Fund and the Ford and Kellogg Foundations led the way with grants for the support of medical education and for feasibility studies for proposed new schools. Several state legislatures also responded by initiating planning studies and appropriating funds for the construction of new schools. Public awareness of the developing shortage of physicians was heightened by three federal commission reports (Bayne-Jones, 1958; Bane, 1959; and Jones, 1960). Using these reports and other unknown calculations, the then surgeon general declared a need for 50,000 additional physicians. Schofield[1] traces in detail the evolution of these developments, which culminated in the initiation of federal support for the expansion of medical education through the Health Professions Education Act of 1963. A key factor was the recognition by the American Medical Association in 1959 that a physician shortage was developing and medical education opportunities should be expanded. However, that association did not endorse federal support for this purpose until several years later. It is of interest that the number of medical school graduates had increased by only 236 per year between 1956 and 1960, and the national need for physicians was being met to an increasing degree in the early 1960s by graduates of foreign medical schools entering the United States at a rate of about 7,000 per year.[2]

For approved construction projects, the Health Professions Assistance Act provided one federal dollar for every local dollar raised for *educational* facilities in existing schools, a two-for-one match for new schools, and also provided for student loan funds. Grants required an increase in the entering class of five percent, or five students, whichever was the greater. Also required was certification of "reasonable assurance" from the Liaison Committee on Medical Education that expansion would not impair the quality of education at the institution concerned. As will be seen, this landmark act, other categorical health manpower legislation that soon followed and the revitalization and leadership of the medical school's Board of Visitors were crucial factors in the growth and expansion of the entire Bowman Gray–Baptist Hospital Medical Center during the ensuing two decades.

At the beginning of the decade of the 1960s, two issues were of paramount importance to the center. The first was the need to correct remaining weaknesses identified by the 1959 accreditation survey; the second was the growing obsolescence and overcrowding of hospital and clinic facilities.

As reflected in these priorities, the medical center was still in a period of "catching up." An important concept was central to our planning philosophy. Surgeon General William Stewart, speaking in the mid-1950s to a small group of Markle scholars who were discussing the relationship of the university to its community, said, "Never forget, an academic medical center is a social institution and if it fails to meet social needs it becomes obsolete." He could have added, "and loses public support."

Medical Center Status 1960

Reid Holmes reported in 1960[3] that the 420-bed Baptist Hospital had served over 17,000 inpatients during the previous year. The 35 outpatient clinics, conducted in facilities built in 1946 for 45,000 patient visits, had accommodated 78,426 visits. Appointments were running two to three weeks behind. Almost 14,000 patients were seen in a two-room emergency area that was totally inadequate. Patients came to the institution from 94 of the 100 North Carolina counties. The major counties involved, in decreasing order, were Forsyth, Surry, Davidson, Wilkes, Stokes and Guilford. Forty percent of inpatient care and 50 percent of outpatient care was charity.

Holmes estimated that the annual cost to the hospital for free care was $500,000, with a like amount representing free professional care by the faculty of the medical school. Mother's Day offerings through the Baptist churches in the state for the care of the needy had reached $215,000. The regular contribution of $129,000 from the cooperative program was being used for funding capital improvements. At that time, the hospital had 1,200 employees and annual expenditures of $3,864,375. The hospital debt totaled $430,000 owed for the purchase of Twin Castles Apartments and renovation of the former nurses home as the Progressive Care Center. The latter was scheduled for completion in March 1961. Holmes indicated this debt was secured by cooperative program funds and "valid" pledges, and would be paid off during the next three years. He listed major facilities needs as a new and larger outpatient facility and emergency room, a modern laundry, expansion of psychiatry beds from 14 to 44, physical rehabilitation facilities, a children's center, and a $1.26 million paramedical school and classroom building. At the time, the hospital, in cooperation with the medical school, conducted training programs for nurse anesthetists, medical technologists, x-ray technicians, practical nurses, medical records librarians and cytotechnologists. There were 78 students in these programs. In addition, the diploma school of nursing had been expanded to 175 students with new housing in Twin Castles. The School of Pastoral Care under the leadership of Dr. Richard K. Young was raising funds through its alumni to purchase much-needed housing and classroom space for student interns and for ministers attending shorter-term training programs.

For the year 1960-1961[4] the medical school reported regular operating expenditures of $3,578,890, of which 42 percent was from sponsored research and training grants, 39 percent from medical service income, and the remainder from basic school funds. This did not include operating expenditures for the Department of Clinics, Amos Cottage and Graylyn, which were budgeted separately.

The full-time faculty was being expanded with special emphasis on the basic medical sciences. The total full-time faculty numbered 104; 33 were in basic science departments and six budgeted positions remained to be filled. Recruitment in the basic sciences had been enhanced by the completion of the Gray and Research Center Buildings, gifts and grants for three named professorships and expansion of library holdings, and by trustee approval for the medical school to advance graduate education to the doctoral level.

In 1960, the medical school had a student body of 215 (46 percent from North Carolina) and admitted 54 students per class. Tuition was $900 per year. The average score of the entering class on the Medical College Admission Test exceeded 500 for the second consecutive year— the highest in the history of the school. There is no question that the Reynolds Scholarship program and the active recruitment efforts, initiated by Dr. J. Maxwell Little several years before, had contributed to this improvement. These activities were further expanded by Dr. Donald M. Hayes, who was appointed assistant dean for Admissions and Premedical relations in July 1960. In addition to medical students, the clinical faculty supervised the training of 11 interns and 85 residents.

The medical school curriculum was under comprehensive study aimed at making medical education more like graduate student education, better integration of the basic and clinical sciences, a reduction in lecture hours and more free and elective time for students.

Graylyn Retreat

Guidelines for the development of the medical school had been established at the 1958 Roanoke (Virginia) retreat, with first priority given to a doubling of the size of the faculty in the basic medical sciences and expanding graduate programs in these areas to the doctoral level. As indicated above, this goal was well within sight in 1960, and planning for Phase II, the development of clinical faculty and facilities, was in order.

A special one-day retreat of the Faculty Executive Council was held at Graylyn in December 1960 to review progress in the two years since the last accreditation survey, to consider an updated faculty effort analysis and to hear reports from hospital administration, the chief of professional services, and department chairmen on needs for the immediate years ahead. The opening statement by the executive dean on problems of the next five years is appended and gives a feeling of the environment and the major challenges of this time (Appendix 1). It was the unanimous conclusion of the participants that orderly planning for Phase II development should begin, and that it should be oriented to the total medical center because of the interdependence of the functions and needs of the two institutions. Immediately following this retreat a Medical Center Planning Committee was established, consisting of the dean (Carpenter), executive dean (Meads), hospital administrator (Holmes), chief of professional services (Alexander) and director of the Department of Clinics (Hardy). Their charge was to project facilities and programs needed during the next 15 to 20 years. An architectural firm was employed to assist the committee in planning. E. Todd Wheeler with Perkins and Will carried out all but the preliminary study which led to final plans of the Medical Center Development program.

Strengthening Institutional Communications

During the 1940s and early 1950s communications within the center were relatively easy due to the small size of the faculty and frequent informal opportunities to exchange information and discuss issues. The Roanoke retreat pointed up the importance of creating more regular and formal processes by which the faculty could be kept abreast of institutional and national academic affairs and become more involved in academic decision making. Several mechanisms were initiated that included faculty forums on medical education and student affairs, broad circulation of the minutes of the weekly Faculty Executive Council meetings, development of a faculty handbook on institutional policies and orientation sessions for new faculty by the executive dean. A medical center Office of Information was established which initiated a monthly *Faculty Information Bulletin* listing faculty grants, publications, scientific presentations and honors; and a quarterly publication, *Medical Alumni Notes (M/A/N)*. In addition, more timely articles about the center were distributed widely to the news media. This office has been under the very able direction of Bill D. Glance, who joined the staff in 1962, and who since that time has won numerous competitive awards for medical center publications at both the state and national levels.

To improve student communications a Student Advisory Council was formed, consisting of the four class presidents, who met regularly with the assistant and executive deans. In the early years of the school the *Journal of the Bowman Gray School of Medicine* was established as a student activity to stimulate student scientific writing and to communicate with alumni. Articles were original research or clinical reviews, but as academic demands on students increased in the 1950s priority for these activities decreased; and soon over 75 percent of the articles were authored by faculty members. The *Journal* was discontinued in June 1961 and replaced with an annual publication *Research and Reviews*. Graduate dissertations and student research reports were published in this journal, edited by students and a faculty advisory committee. It was discontinued in 1969.

Program Cost Study

As mentioned before, the Congress had begun hearings on federal assistance required if the supply of physicians and other health manpower was to be increased to meet future needs. There was no reasonable estimate of the cost of medical education. Such information had become particularly difficult to generate because of the multiple and overlapping programs developing in each academic medical center. With foundation support, the Association of American Medical Colleges undertook a program cost study under the direction of Mr. A.J. Carroll, business manager of Upstate Medical Center (Syracuse). Bowman Gray was one of 15 schools selected for the study, because it had already developed a method to estimate faculty time devoted to its various programs. With minor modification, our approach became a "faculty effort analysis," which served as the basis for the actual cost determinations. Carroll spent a week with us discussing objectives and methodology. The keen mind and experience of Harry O. Parker, controller, made a major contribution to this effort. The study was conducted for the year 1959–1960. At Bowman Gray the estimated cost of medical education was $2,634 per student per year. As tuition was $900 per year, the student was paying 34 percent of the cost, and the school was subsidizing the remainder through endowment income, gifts, medical service income and other sources. It was calculated that this subsidy represented an estimated $375,000 for each graduating class. The cost of medical education at Bowman Gray turned out to be very similar to that at the Emory and Syracuse Medical Schools. As a result, the AAMC made the case before Congress that the beneficiaries of the subsidy were the student and society and, as raising tuition significantly was not possible, financial assistance from Congress (representing society) was essential if more physicians were to be produced by new and expanded medical schools.

Faculty effort analyses and cost studies were continued periodically at the medical school, serving as valuable guides to the development of fiscal policies, in justifying to governing boards the relatively high cost of operating a school of medicine and as an assist in fund-raising. Mr. Parker found the cost study approach a sound basis for negotiating indirect costs related to federal grants. It proved to be useful at a later date in securing state aid to expand opportunities for North Carolinians to study medicine at Bowman Gray and Duke Schools of Medicine.

Further Evolution of the Medical Service Plan

The corporate practice of medicine and the related issue of how medical schools were handling medical service income became a focus of concern of the American Medical Association in the late 1950s. The AAMC was also worried that charity patients used predominantly for teaching were diminishing because of the growth of health insurance plans. This was occurring at a time when schools were feeling pressure to expand student bodies to help meet projected physician shortages. The two associations met and developed principles for handling fees for medical service which were published in 1959. The Bowman Gray medical service plan was consistent with these principles and operated as follows:

1. The financial and business affairs of the clinical practice were the responsibility of the Department of Clinics, a service department of the medical school. Its director was a member of the faculty appointed by, and responsible to, the dean. A committee of faculty for the clinic served in an advisory capacity to the director and dean.
2. Medical service was organized under a plan of group endeavor by department or section which was approved by the dean and the chairman and members of the department or section concerned.

Such a plan could not impair academic excellence, render an injustice, or threaten the public relations of the institution.

3. The budgets of all departments participating in medical service consisted of basic school funds, gifts and grants, and fees for service that were subject to periodic review and annual audit like all other units of the school, and incorporated in the financial statement submitted to the university president and trustees each year.

4. Individual physicians retained the prerogative of establishing fees; however, the clinic director could modify the fee if it were deemed excessive.

5. The school endorsed the "incentive principle," i.e., recognition of variation in individual efficiency in patient care, as well as in teaching and research.

6. Institutional ceilings were not placed on incomes; however, time spent in practice was limited and emphasis was placed on expected and actual contribution of individuals, sections, and departments, rather than income.

7. Full-time clinical faculty were provided offices and examining areas in the center without charge and, except for the occasional outside consultation, restricted all of their medical service activity to the medical center. In most instances, patient examining areas were centralized and separated from space assigned to a department for academic activities. Charges for clinic services, secretarial assistance, and other usual and necessary expenses were deducted from gross income before crediting it to the departmental budget. Since 1954, faculty involved in fee-for-service activity had pledged voluntarily four percent of gross income from professional service to the building fund, which had assisted in the construction of the South Wing of the hospital and expansion of medical school facilities. Additional voluntary deductions by department or section were used as research and development funds held and administered by the school. Together, these funds made a very significant contribution to the medical center. Unlike many medical schools, all private as well as charity patients were utilized for teaching, since the founding of the four-year school.

In 1960 increasing concern was expressed over the inability of the school to develop a plan which would permit members of the full-time faculty who were solely or primarily dependent on income from fees-for-service, to set aside on a tax-deferred basis a portion of earnings for future retirement. Dr. Frank R. Lock served as chairman of a committee commissioned to study national legislation, experiences of group practice clinics, and to consult with tax, insurance and legal authorities. The goals were the creation of an adequate retirement plan, and the expansion of the meager fringe benefit program, in order to enhance faculty morale and stability. Mr. Robert Stockton, a Winston-Salem lawyer, was the key advisor during this period. The committee reported its findings and recommendations in February 1962. In essence, it was determined that when a bona fide employer-employee relation existed, the school could provide an extensive fringe benefit program on a tax-free basis and also develop deferred income or pension plans on a tax-deferred basis. To satisfy the tax code and obtain these objectives, it was advised that participating faculty would have to be salaried under an employer-employee contract with the school. This would be superimposed on the existing medical service plan, with the amount of fee-for-service income after expenses in a guaranteed salary component, set at a level below expected earnings. Individual overages after subtracting a pro rata share of fringe benefit costs, the building pledge and R & D fund allocations, would then be returned to an individual every six months as a bonus (later every three months). This preserved the important incentive principle. It was proposed that basic science faculty and key administrative personnel be included as contract employees, though the portion of the plan related to medical service income was of course not pertinent.

The plan was debated by the clinical faculty both formally and informally. At the faculty meeting in May 1962, the executive dean stated that it is only natural and proper that each individual consider the new plan on the basis of how it would affect each of them personally. However, he stated his conviction that the new plan was of tremendous importance not only to the future development of every department, but also to the national stature of the school in the eyes of educational associations, government agencies and foundations on which we must depend for our support. Clyde Hardy again served throughout this period as an effective communications link with the clinical faculty. The proposed comprehensive insurance plan and the Teachers Insurance and Annuity (TIAA) retirement program were discussed with insurance representatives both on a group and individual basis. The Keogh Plan at that time was quite restrictive, limiting set-asides to $2,500 of which half was taxable. One key to the acceptance of the new financial plan was that it was offered on a *voluntary* basis to existing faculty, but was required for all who joined the faculty after the date it became effective.

A letter from the IRS dated December 7, 1962 officially approved an employer-employee relationship under the proposed plan and the organization and policies of the school, and it was implemented after trustee approval on January 3, 1963. Initially, over 90 percent of eligible faculty participated and, by the following year, only three continued under their original arrangements. The success of the plan attracted national attention and during the ensuing years Mr. Hardy was asked to consult on medical service plan development at many medical schools. He later served as chairman of a task force of the AAMC assessing these plans in American medical schools and he summarized the findings in a paper.[5]

Other Significant Events Before Re-accreditation

In 1961, Donald M. Hayes requested return to full-time academic duties; and Dr. Robert L. Tuttle, who had served as chairman of the Department of Microbiology, became assistant dean for Student Affairs. In this position, which he held until 1970, he was to begin a long and distinguished career in medical school administration, which continued in 1970 at the newly developing University of Texas Health Sciences Center in Houston, at which he became dean.

Mrs. Nathalie Gray Bernard, a member of the original committee that administered the Bowman Gray Fund and a continuing benefactor of the medical school and hospital, died at the age of 77 on November 28, 1961. Her will included a bequest of $1,319,000 to the medical school as endowment. The income was used initially to liquidate the $410,000 debt remaining as the result of the construction of the Research Center Building and renovation of the original facilities.

In March 1962 the family of R. Gardner Kellogg established a memorial in his name—an endowment fund of $600,000 to implement a program in physical medicine and rehabilitation at the medical center. Dr. Edwin Martinat was appointed director of the program.

A three-year comprehensive study of the curriculum under the direction of Dr. Charles L. Spurr, chairman of the Committee on Medical Education, was completed and its implementation was begun. As previously noted, emphasis was placed on a graduate education model for medical education that included an increase in free time for students and a decrease in laboratory and lecture time, the addition of an elective quarter to the fourth year, a senior thesis, student research opportunities, and more time for instruction in behavioral medicine. In an attempt to reduce competition for grades, the faculty introduced a system of evaluation which eliminated the reporting of numerical rankings to students by translating them into three categories for each course, i.e., pass, low pass, and fail. Several years later a fourth category—honors—was added. Internship programs throughout the country continued to demand the class standings of applicants, so that numerical grades for students were maintained in the registrar's office for this purpose alone. Dean Davison of Duke Medical School refused to meet this requirement, and his letters classified all Duke medical students in the upper half of the class. When asked how this could occur, he replied that Duke accepted only students who would be in the upper half of the class.

Accreditation Survey, December 1962

The extraordinary efforts of all concerned toward correcting the deficiencies apparent during the accreditation survey of January 1959 were recognized during a resurvey in December 1962. During this four-year period 108,000 square feet had been added to the medical school, the number of basic science faculty had doubled and the total faculty increased by more than 50 percent. Ph.D. programs had been established in four basic science areas, 13,500 volumes had been added to the library, a new curriculum was being implemented and finances had been strengthened through major gifts and bequests. The survey team also commented favorably on the evolution of the medical service plan and department of clinics, overall faculty morale, and the vivarium which had become a national model under the leadership of Dr. Thomas Clarkson. As a result the survey team, under the chairmanship of Dr. William N. Hubbard, Jr., then dean of the University of Michigan, recommended complete and full accreditation with special commendation for the development of faculty and academic programs that had occurred since the prior survey.

Concerns were expressed, however, on the overcrowding of inpatient and out-patient facilities, and the need for a selective expansion of the clinical faculty. This would be critical to approval by the Liaison Committee on Medical Education if the school expected to expand the medical student body to assist in meeting the emerging social need for more physicians and other health manpower.

In the summary sessions of the survey team with the dean and executive dean and later with President Tribble, it was suggested that, in keeping with the "national understanding of titles," Dr. Meads should be called dean and Dr. Carpenter, who had been functioning as a vice president of medical affairs, might assume this or a similar title. At Dr. Carpenter's request, these changes were approved the following day by the president and became effective January 11, 1963.

A Joint Planning Effort to Meet Social Needs

The Medical Center Planning Committee had been meeting regularly since March 1962 with architectural consultants and a special committee on clinical faculty development. Parameters of a major facilities expansion and renovation program were emerging. For the medical school they included a 30 percent increase in the medical student body, a modest increase in graduate and postdoctoral students, greater emphasis on continuing medical education and faculty and staff expansion to meet the projected increases in academic and patient care responsibilities. For the hospital, need focused on new and expanded ambulatory care and emergency facilities, two hundred additional hospital beds, a major expansion of support services and a paramedical school. These objectives necessitated also a major land acquisition program, a new power plant to supply heat and air-conditioning, and expanded parking facilities. Several committees of the faculty were involved in defining facilities criteria for improved teaching in the ambulatory setting and for the introduction of new teaching and student support mechanisms. These included multi-purpose laboratories for students in the basic medical sciences popularized by Western Reserve University School of Medicine, individual student study cubicles, rooms for small group teaching, a center-wide closed circuit television network, and a 400-seat auditorium to replace the ancient amphitheater that would be demolished.

Reid Holmes and Dr. Ernest Yount, respectively, obtained grants from the Hartford Foundation to establish small intensive care and renal dialysis units in the hospital to meet an immediate need and also to gain experience to guide the planning process. A grant from the Booth Ferris Foundation allowed George Lynch, director of Medical

Illustrations, to purchase basic television production equipment and plan for a center-wide television network as an adjunct to teaching.

Meanwhile the medical school received a grant from the National Institutes of Health to assist in the construction of a three-story, 10,080-square-foot addition to the vivarium. This allowed the consolidation of animal facilities and freed up space on the fifth floor of the Research Center Building for a major expansion of the Department of Microbiology. Dr. Quentin Myrvik (University of Virginia) was recruited as chairman in 1963 to develop this department, giving particular emphasis to the expanding field of immunology.

The first estimate of the cost of the Medical Center Development program was $15 million for facilities and land acquisition and $15 million for endowment to support faculty development and charity patient care. It was estimated that up to 50 percent of the costs of construction could be obtained from existing federal programs and pending legislation to support the expansion of medical education facilities, which included teaching hospitals as well as health professions schools.

From the beginning, it was recognized that it would be necessary to obtain the approval of the Baptist State Convention for the hospital to receive federal grants for construction and that a strong and dedicated group of lay leaders would be essential to assist in raising the funds necessary from private sources.

Hospital Approved by the Convention to Accept Federal Funds

As noted previously, obtaining convention approval for the hospital to accept federal grants was a delicate question, as such funds had been rejected for the South Wing in a special meeting of the convention in April 1952. Dr. Carpenter and Reid Holmes worked quietly behind the scenes with key leaders of the convention on this matter in early 1962 with the able assistance of the Rev. Dewey Hobbs, then president of the convention's General Board. Because policies established by the convention in 1957 allowed the medical school to accept federal grants, it was deemed that approval of such grants to the Baptist Hospital was the prerogative of the convention's General Board, to be brought to the attention of the convention as a whole only as a matter of information. At its meeting in January 1963 the general board approved a statement of its executive committee relative to the use of government funds by the Baptist Hospital. The first paragraph of this statement was as follows:

> The Executive Committee received the request of the representatives of the Baptist Hospital as herein outlined, and based upon information presented and the assurances of Baptist Hospital representatives that the facility herein proposed is no different from the programs and grants for research facilities previously accepted by the Bowman Gray School of Medicine of Wake Forest College, the Executive Committee offers no objection.[6]

The statement then stipulated the usual requirements in accord with policy related to not pledging hospital real estate as security to the government, not signing any agreement that gave government control over the facility, complying with the "for full services rendered" concept, and furnishing full reports to the board. It is of interest that the initial paragraph refers to facilities and programs for research and not for patient care. However, in the statement of requirements, it refers to not entering into agreements which would give the federal government control over "any research structure or structure herein contemplated." This wording of course broadened the functional use "of a facility supported by federal funds" and serves as an indication that the entire statement was carefully crafted in the light of past history.

The Hill-Burton Act had been modified in 1961 to include a "non-interference" clause and, as a result, this source of federal-state funds was now deemed acceptable under the action of the general board. No comments were received on this matter when it was reported to the full convention. Debate instead focused on Dr. Tribble and a Wake Forest resolution to add non-Baptists to the college trustees, which did not receive the two-thirds vote required. Approval was given, however, for the trustees of the college "to change the name of the College to Wake Forest University at the appropriate time."

A year later the convention approved the request of the seven Baptist colleges in North Carolina that they be permitted to participate in grants from the Higher Education Act of 1963. In 1965 resolutions were approved to allow interim borrowing by Baptist Hospital ($1.5 million) and Wake Forest ($725,000) for the medical center expansion program.

The Board of Visitors—A Vital Contribution to the Medical Center

The original external advisory council to the dean had met intermittently during most of the 1940s. As noted, because Bowman Gray, Jr. and Gordon Gray volunteered for military service, James A. Gray, Sr. served as the principal advisor to the dean. Bowman Gray, Jr., who followed James A. Gray as president of Reynolds Tobacco Company, became chairman of the group from 1952 to 1960. Richard J. Reynolds, James G. Hanes, Charles H. Babcock and Albert L. Butler, Jr. were added to the council in 1955. Gordon Gray resigned in 1950 when he became president of the University of North Carolina. In September 1958 the group voted to change its name to the Board of Visitors of the Bowman Gray School of Medicine and to meet regularly on a quarterly basis to hear progress reports from the dean and his associates. Richard Reynolds resigned in 1959 because of health reasons which had confined him to his home on Sapelo Island, Georgia. His interest in the medical school continued, however, until his death in December 1964. Bowman Gray, Jr.'s health was declining also due to a progressive neuromuscular disease and, though he remained active, the chairmanship of the Board of Visitors was turned over to James A. Gray, Jr. for the year 1960-1961. Bowman Gray then asked Albert Butler, president of Arista Mills and very active in community affairs, to accept the chairmanship of the group. He served in this position until 1969. This was a most fortunate appointment, as Butler brought a leadership that not only led to the revitalization and expansion of the board, but also he gave sensitive and wise counsel to the administration of the school and hospital at a very critical time in the development of the medical center.

It was evident that the Board of Visitors of the medical school was the only viable means of developing the strong leadership that was essential to raising the funds from private sources that would be needed for the expansion program. At this time, with few exceptions, the trustees of the hospital and college were not selected for their fund-raising ability or close contacts with large corporations or foundations. They were selected primarily as representatives of urban and rural Baptist churches throughout the state. Important additions were made to the Board of Visitors during the next two years that included Ralph Hanes, William Conrad, Irving Carlyle, William Lybrook and Mrs. Anne Reynolds Forsyth. Gordon Gray, who had served as secretary of the Army in the Eisenhower administration following his term as president the University of North Carolina, agreed to rejoin the board in 1962. A series of educational programs was presented at board meetings that included information on the growth and development of the medical center, the recent cost study that for the first time allowed valid comparisons with other institutions, data on the projected manpower shortage and pending federal legislation on this problem and, finally, the general requirements of the medical school and hospital if they were to assist in meeting health manpower needs and the increasing demands for more sophisticated patient care services.

At their meeting in September 1962 the Board of Visitors declared an interest in moving ahead with plans for the development of the medical school and indicated that this interest extended also to Baptist Hospital. This action marked the emergence of a strong and dedicated group of community leaders whose concern focused on the entire medical center. Ketchum, Inc. was employed to conduct a preliminary survey of the fund-raising potential for the medical center development program. Gorman Mattison, vice president of the company, reported to the Board of Visitors and trustee representatives of both institutions that raising the anticipated $7 million for construction from private sources was feasible but that, in addition to local funds, board help would be needed in reaching out for funds from other communities. He further stated that Duke Medical Center was considering a $60 million expansion program and that a University of North Carolina campaign was pending, so that a great deal of educational work must be done if the center was to reach its goal. On May 8, 1963 the Board of Visitors recommended that trustees proceed with a $15 million expansion program for land acquisition and medical center facilities and pledged full support to raise half of this amount. The remainder was expected from federal matching funds. Ketchum, Inc. was recommended as fund-raising counsel for the campaign. Shortly thereafter both trustee bodies endorsed these recommendations enthusiastically. Bowman and Gordon Gray gave an immediate gift of $84,000 to cover the estimated cost of the campaign and Mr. Charles Wheeler was assigned as campaign director.

As will be seen, a very crucial decision was made to ask Mr. John F. Watlington, Jr., president of Wachovia Bank and Trust Company, to serve as chairman of the Medical Center Development campaign. The request was made without his prior knowledge at the home of Bowman Gray in September 1963. Mr. Watlington indicated that he was greatly honored, but would like time to consider the matter and to meet with the entire Board of Visitors. At that meeting several days later he noted that, despite the fine reputation of the medical center, it would take an unusual effort on the part of the entire board to raise the $7 million required for the facilities expansion program, and requested that each member let him know how much support they were prepared to give to the campaign. The forthcoming commitments in both time and financial support quickly demonstrated the remarkable dedication of the entire group, and Mr. Watlington accepted the chairmanship and membership on the board. Years later he joked that he had little choice, as Bowman Gray was chairman of the Compensation Committee of the Wachovia Board of Directors. Public announcement of the campaign was made on October 19, 1963.

Mr. Watlington enlisted Mr. Gordon Hanes as general cochairman of the campaign, and appointed Ralph P. Hanes chairman of primary gifts; Mrs. Anne Forsyth and William Lybrook, cochairmen of initial gifts; and Marion J. Davis, chairman of major gifts. Gordon Gray served as chairman of national gifts. The remainder of the board participated actively where their special contacts proved valuable.

Unfortunately, Coy Carpenter suffered his first heart attack in May 1963 and a second in January 1964, leaving him unable to participate actively in the campaign. However, his skillful work with the leadership of the Baptist State Convention prior to these episodes was largely responsible for allowing Baptist Hospital to accept federal funds for the expansion program.

Initial emphasis in fund raising was given to Forsyth County and its major corporations, foundations and selected individuals. It was known that, because of the community's outstanding record of philanthropy, the first question in out-of-county solicitations would be, "What has Forsyth County contributed?" An important initial stimulus to the campaign was a pledge of $1,250,000 by the clinical faculty. Although Wake Forest had made a commitment not to seek funds in Forsyth County for ten years after their recent campaign, Albert Butler obtained approval from the county solicitations committee, as the group did not consider this pledge of the college binding on the medical school-hospital complex. This decision established a principle that, from the fund-raising point of view, was to serve both Wake Forest and the medical center well in the future. The strong endorsement and assistance of Mr. Charles Babcock was important also through his influence in coordinating gifts from the two major foundations in the community.

Meanwhile, prior to the announcement of the expansion plans of the center, the acquisition of adjacent land to the north and west was proceeding quietly under the supervision of Reid Holmes. He was assisted by Leon Lentz of Wachovia Bank and Trust Company, who negotiated purchases in the name of Northwest Realty Company. Twenty-eight high-priority acres were purchased for $640,000.

1964–1965—A Banner Year

By June 1965, $8,701,103 had been raised for the development program from private sources, and architectural plans were in the stage of design development. Eighty-five percent of these funds had come from corporations, foundations, the clinical faculty and individuals in Forsyth County—an amount far greater than that raised in any previous campaigns in this area. It was truly a remarkable effort and response. In his final report Wheeler, the director of the campaign, echoed the feelings of all concerned when he said, "It is hard to realize how Mr. Watlington could have done more without resigning from the banking business." He further pointed out that the campaign demonstrated the strengths of a joint hospital-medical school approach to fund raising, and the appeal of the medical center concept, i.e., presenting the institutions as a unified medical center involving closely interrelated programs of teaching, research and patient care. Although success seemed near at this time, the story does not end here, as will be reported later.

Although the remarkable success of the campaign was the principal highlight of this fiscal year, several other events were of major importance. A second faculty retreat was held September 3–5, 1964 in Blowing Rock, North Carolina. One-hundred-five members of the faculty and administration of the school and hospital attended. Harold Tribble, Edwin Wilson and John L. Caughey, associate dean at Western Reserve University School of Medicine, participated actively as guests. Agenda topics included, "Goals and Priorities in the Development of the Medical School during the Next Ten Years," "Goals and Methods of Clinical Teaching in the Four-year Curriculum with Emphasis on Ambulant Patients," and "Evaluation of Medical Students and Performance." Drs. Emery Miller and Robert Tuttle were chairmen of committees that developed extensive background material for the last two topics, respectively; data for the first were compiled by the medical center planning committee. Extensive proceedings of the retreat were circulated to the faculty and served as valuable background for the design of both the facilities and the educational program. Shortly after the retreat Dr. Tuttle was advanced to associate dean, with his responsiblities expanded to include the program of medical education. Clyde Hardy was appointed associate dean (Administration) in recognition that his administrative activities had extended well beyond the management of the Department of Clinics.

With the growth of animal research, the need for expansion to a farm area became urgent. In July 1964 Thomas Clarkson located 128 acres of land in the Friedberg area near the Davidson-Forsyth County lines, a fifteen-minute drive from the center. The purchase price and cost of basic functional improvements was $83,720. This was amortized over several years through fees from research projects that involved the use of the farm. The wisdom of this acquisition was proven in subsequent years through the remarkable development of laboratory animal medicine as an integral part of the research and graduate program of the school and the national reputation and financial support that it generated under Clarkson's leadership.

Medical Center Desegregation

The winds of broad social change that culminated in the Civil Rights Act of 1964 were evident in the beginning of this decade. In April 1961 the Wake Forest trustees approved the request of the medical, law and graduate schools to admit qualified applicants without regard to race. The Faculty Executive Council believed that the admission of blacks to the medical school should wait until integration of clinical facilities had been accomplished, which was planned to coincide with the expansion program. However, with the signing of the Civil Rights Act, which became effective on July 2, 1964, Section 601 of this law provided that "no person in the United States shall, on the grounds of race, color, or national origin be excluded from participation in, be denied the benefits of, or be subject to discrimination under any program or activity receiving federal financial assistance." On July 14, 1964 a memorandum from the Department of Health, Education and Welfare suggested that all institutions review present policies and practices so they would be in a position to provide assurances necessary to comply with regulations relative to Section 601 when issued.

On July 29, 1964, the Faculty Executive Council adopted as school-wide policy the wording of Section 601, adding the words at the end "conducted by The Bowman Gray School of Medicine." Baptist Hospital also adopted a desegregation policy and in December 1964 the dean reported to the Board of Visitors that a policy of total integration within the medical center had been accomplished, that black patients were being admitted on all clinical services, and that several black nurses and technicians were employed. This was done without any newspaper publicity. The first black medical student, William Grimes, was admitted in September 1967 and graduated in May 1972. The first black graduate student, Cynthia Wells Krishna, was admitted to the master's degree program in microbiology in 1968.

Members of the faculty had long served as consultants to physicians at the Kate B. Reynolds Memorial Hospital, where black patients of Forsyth County were hospitalized. The lack of supporting services had made this difficult. Dr. Richard Myers recalls a number of instances during the 1950s in which emergency surgery was required, black patients being then admitted to Baptist Hospital. They were officially classified by the clinical faculty as Indians, notwithstanding the disbelief of the operating room supervisor, who had no choice but to defer to the authority of the attending physician.

The first full-time black faculty member was Dr. William Quivers, who was appointed associate professor of pediatrics in July 1967.

Inter-University Relations

A new era in relationships among the three medical schools in North Carolina was initiated at this time. Dr. William Anlyan had replaced Wilburt C. Davison as dean of Duke University School of Medicine, and Isaac Taylor had followed Reece Berryhill as dean at the University of North Carolina School of Medicine. The deans of the three schools, who had known each other as Markle Scholars, met one evening in September 1964 during the annual meeting of the Association of American Medical Colleges in Denver, Colorado. It was felt that the relative isolation and provincialism of the three academic medical centers and the occasional divisive relationships with organized medicine were inappropriate in a time of rapid advances in medical sciences and well-documented health care needs in the state. As Anlyan put it, "Let's fight on the football field but work together to assist in improving health care for all North Carolinians."

It was decided that the first joint effort would be the coordination and expansion of continuing education for physicians, which would be named Project ICE (Inter-university Continuing Education). Although this effort did not evolve under this name, it was absorbed quickly the following year under the new federally-financed Regional Medical Program for Heart Disease, Cancer and Stroke in association with the State Medical Society. The deans had learned to "shift gears" quickly when new money became available.

To help resolve several controversial issues dividing academe and the medical profession, the deans requested a meeting with the State Board of Medical Examiners in 1965. This unusual request came as a surprise to board members but, because of the mutually beneficial exchange in information that occurred, such meetings have been held annually since that time.

As will be seen, these cooperative efforts continued to evolve and expand in the years ahead through mechanisms that included the North Carolina Joint Conference Committee on Medical Care, quarterly meetings of the three (and now four) medical centers and the highly successful Area Health Education Center programs.

The Mid-sixties — Prelude to Complexity and Crisis

The political and social climate in the nation in 1965 presaged changes that would have both positive and negative influences on the medical center and pose increasingly complex challenges. By this time, the United States involvement in Vietnam, both militarily and financially, was accelerating rapidly. At home, President Lyndon Johnson was implementing successfully his legislative program termed "the war on poverty" and "the Great Society" with major commitments of federal funds for education, health, urban renewal and the like. In 1963, Congress had declared that health was a human right and that all citizens should have equal access to high-quality medical care at reasonable cost. Although the nation continued to invest heavily in hospitals, biomedical research and the expansion of health manpower, the next major step toward this goal was to improve access to care for the poor and the elderly by reducing financial barriers. In the heady climate of the "Great Society," Congress in 1965 legislated Medicare and Medicaid despite the long-standing opposition of organized medicine to any form of national health insurance. These two programs did indeed move the poor and elderly into the mainstream of medical care and brought, with associated regulations, a new source of income to hospitals and physicians. However, they

91

also changed the attitudes of providers and philanthropy toward charity care. Numerous other categorical federal health programs were spawned during this and the following few years that included neighborhood clinics, mental health centers, and programs for child health, migrant workers, nutrition, rehabilitation, retardation, alcoholism, etc. To speed up the transfer of new scientific knowledge to practicing physicians, the Regional Medical Program for Heart Disease, Cancer and Stroke was initiated in 1965. There was a growing awareness, however, that these categorical approaches, though politically successful, were resulting in fragmentation of the medical care system. As such, in 1966 the Partnership for Health Act was enacted to initiate comprehensive health planning at the state and local levels in an attempt to rationalize the health care system.

Many of these new programs were potential sources of new funds for academic medical centers to enhance services to their communities and states. On the other hand, they posed problems related to institutional priorities, diffusion of effort, autonomy and program balance. Already by 1965, over 50 percent of all funds spent by medical schools was derived from federal grants and contracts. These funds, primarily from the National Institutes of Health, did not cover adequately the associated indirect costs of the sponsored programs. When they were used as primary salary support for the faculty involved, there were some instances of loyalties divided between the institution and the granting agency and spawned what some termed the "academic entrepreneur."

Of far greater import, however, was the subsequent impact of this so-called "guns and butter" era on the future of the national economy and on the cost of medical education and medical care.

A study on the future role of the Association of American Medical Colleges entitled *Planning for Medical Progress Through Education* appeared in 1965 and proved of major importance to the future of medical education in this country.[7] The study, chaired by Dr. Lowell T. Coggeshall, vice president of the University of Chicago, was thereafter known as the "Coggeshall Report." The study found widespread concern about the problems of medical education, including the multiplicity of organizations that were planning programs and policies to solve the shortage of health manpower. It noted broad support among educators, public officials, and others "for some organization—preferably the AAMC—to assume a more aggressive and correlative role if the future needs in the field of education for all health personnel are to be met." Up until this time the association had been largely regarded as a "deans' club." Recommendations included a major reorganization to include university presidents, representatives of medical school faculty, teaching hospitals, and students, unification of all phases of medical education under university control, and strong representation at the national level including the moving of the association's headquarters from Chicago to Washington. Although all recommendations were not implemented during the next few years, the AAMC expanded its constituencies by forming separate Councils of Deans, Academic Societies (faculty members), and Teaching Hospitals, and an Organization of Student Representatives. In 1969 it completed its move to Washington, D.C., where Dr. John A.D. Cooper became full-time president. Under his remarkable leadership, the Association enlarged its professional staff, information base and services, and soon became the dominant voice for medical education in this country.

References and Notes

1. Schofield, J.R., New and Expanded Medical Schools, Mid-Century to the 1980s—a publication of the Association of American Medical Colleges, Jossey Bass Publishers, San Francisco, CA, 1984, pages 11–31.

2. Lewis, I.J. and Sheps, C.G. The Sick Citadel: The American Academic Medical Center and the Public Interest; Oelgeschlager, Gunn, and Hain Publishers, Inc., Cambridge, MA, 1983.

3. Report to Medical School Board of Visitors, October 12, 1960, and Annual of the Baptist State Convention of North Carolina, pp. 164–165; and Annual Report of Outpatient Department, 1960.

4. 1960-61 Annual Report to Trustees and Report of Liaison Committee on Medical Education for 1960–61.

5. Hardy, C.T. Group Practice by Medical School Faculty; Journal of Medical Education, 43:8 (August) 1968.

6. Annual of the Baptist State Convention of North Carolina, 1963, p. 54.

7. Coggeshall, L.T., Planning for Medical Progress Through Education; A report submitted to the Executive Council of the Association of American Medical Colleges, April 1965.

CHAPTER VI

Weathering A Storm
(1966–1971)

By the fall of 1965 the combined effects of the Vietnam war and new Great Society programs began to take their toll on the national economy. Domestic shortages in manpower, equipment and supplies were forcing up wages and prices. The increase in the minimum wage from $1.25 in step-wise fashion to $1.60 per hour by 1968 had a major effect on not-for-profit hospitals that had employed large numbers of workers at or near minimum levels. The most immediate impact on the medical center was reflected in the operating budget of the hospital and on the projected cost of the medical center development program.

Medical Center Development Program

At this point it should be remembered that, in planning a facilities expansion program that involved federal funds, one first estimated the cost of the project from preliminary architectural drawings, then raised the estimated nonfederal matching funds and finally applied for federal grants. Construction could begin only after notification of the federal award. As noted, by June 1965, the estimated funds required for the medical center development program had been raised, architectural plans were in the design development phase and applications for matching grants from two federal programs were submitted in the fall. A joint site visit by two agencies was scheduled for January 1966. Construction was to proceed in several phases over a six-year period beginning in July 1967.

At the urging of fund-raising counsel, the first medical center professional development officer was employed in December 1965 to begin planning for the endowment phase of the program. He was Howard Hall, director of development, Vanderbilt University Medical Center.

By early 1966 the architects alerted the center that cost of construction which had been increasing at approximately 1% to 2% per year was now rising at 1% to 2% per month. Major budget revisions were made and a decision was reached to defer temporarily the paramedical school project. In March the trustees and Board of Visitors were informed that the projected cost of the revised program was $26,900,000. As the hospital phase of construction was not scheduled to begin until August 1968 a large part of the increase was associated with this element. All agreed, however, that the center should proceed, intensify efforts to raise additional funds, and delay the endowment phase of the campaign.

Meanwhile President Tribble, noting the importance of the Board of Visitors to the medical school, was developing similar boards for the college, law and business schools, and had begun a $2-million fund-raising drive for a new stadium. He had announced also that he was planning a $72-million campaign for the Reynolda campus. Groves Stadium was built, but the fund-raising effort was disappointing. The larger campaign did not materialize, but was reconstituted with a much lower goal by Tribble's successor at a later date.

In December 1966 it was decided to request an increase in the federal medical education facilities grants for the hospital and school, based on the unexpected increase in the costs of construction. Albert Butler accompanied representatives of the center and the architect to Washington, D.C. for this purpose. The agency was not aware of the cost increase, but got immediate confirmation by telephone from regional offices that our information was correct. An increase in the grant from $6,627,612 to $9,784,079 was negotiated on the condition that the center commit to raise the additional funds required to complete the project. As no trustee member was present, and as we did not want the agency to reassess this generous offer later, Albert Butler gave them the commitment. We immediately visited Gordon Gray at his Washington office, and he concurred with the action, as did the trustees and board of visitors soon after. Although the research facilities agency could not, by law, make similar grant adjustments, they later were able to make a supplemental grant for a clinical research unit and support laboratories in the new facilities.

By July 1967 the low bid by Kane Construction Company of $7,292,704 for the 122,000-square-foot, five-floor addition to the medical school, the 400-seat auditorium, and the new power plant was accepted and construction was under way. These components were completed by September 1969 in time for the arrival of the enlarged freshman class of 76 students. Meanwhile, a value engineering company was employed to develop options to reduce the hospital cost through deferral of elements and quality reductions, and fund raising continued. By July 1968 $21,937,826 was on hand and $2 million more was assured from the North Carolina Medical Care Commission in January 1969, in addition to $265,000 from the Appalachian Regional Commission.

Reid Holmes and the hospital trustees had decided to move ahead separately with the $2.5 million, 55,000-square-foot, three-story paramedical school building. This project was financed by grants from the Nursing Education Facilities Branch of the Bureau of Health Manpower Education, several corporations and by pledging future receipts from the Cooperative Program. The building was occupied in September 1969.

By May 1969 $25.9 million was on hand, and it was estimated that at least $5 million more would be needed to finance the hospital phase and renovations. Ketchum, Inc. was employed again for a statewide campaign to raise this amount; and Thomas H. Davis, president of Piedmont Airlines, accepted the Phase II chairmanship. Colin Stokes, president of Reynolds Tobacco Company and chairman of the hospital trustees, served as vice chairman. In discussions on the strategy for this second effort, Albert Butler pointed out that the names of the medical school and hospital inferred to some potential donors that the Gray family and the Baptist denomination were the major supporters of the institutions when, in fact, others had made very large contributions to programs and capital campaigns. He suggested that new buildings within the complex be named to honor those past contributors. With the approval of trustees and donors, the hospital tower was named for the Z. Smith Reynolds Foundation, the medical school addition for the Hanes family, and the auditorium for Charles H. Babcock. Although a major contributor over many years, the R.J. Reynolds Tobacco Company did not wish to be so identified.

All members of the Board of Visitors participated actively in this second phase, including four new members—Mrs. Barbara L. Hanes, Mrs. Winifred Babcock, Mr. James Glenn and Mr. William Cash.

Anne Forsyth had resigned earlier to join the Wake Forest College Development Council. During this successful fund-raising effort, local foundations, major corporations and many individuals made additional contributions; and Tom Davis and the dean made numerous presentations throughout the state—Davis piloting his own plane on these occasions, weather permitting. Many new donors joined the program and this second effort raised over $7 million.

At this point, the story must return again to the mid-sixties in order to describe other important events that were occurring simultaneously within the school and hospital as a result of the nationwide economic and social pressures of this time.

Escalating Hospital Problems

The national impact on hospital costs due to wage-price inflation that began during the last half of the 1960s deeply affected Baptist Hospital. In the trustee report to the convention in November 1968 it was stated that the hospital had been experiencing deficits over the past three years and financial difficulty was severe. The convention was warned that this could lead to a decrease in the number of beds set aside for service patients and would require advance payments or welfare agency certification for both clinic and inpatients.[1]

Colin Stokes, president and chief executive officer of Reynolds Tobacco Company, became chairman of the hospital trustees in January 1969 and a member of the Board of Visitors. Since representatives of the medical school were not invited to attend hospital trustee meetings, there was no awareness in the medical faculty of the severity of the financial crisis that had developed in the hospital. In August 1969 it became apparent that the hospital administrator was developing overt signs of Alzheimer's disease, and the dean and Eben Alexander, chief of professional services, so informed Mr. Stokes. Subsequent examinations here and elsewhere confirmed this diagnosis—an immense tragedy in view of Mr. Holmes' relatively young age (51 years) and his outstanding devotion and contributions to the center since 1945.

Immediate steps were taken by Mr. Stokes to strengthen financial management and to recruit a qualified administrator to fill the position of chief executive officer of the hospital. It was agreed that Mr. Holmes would stay on with the title of president and be kept involved as long as feasible. At the same time the medical school was made fully aware of the hospital's severe financial difficulty. Mr. Richard E. Held, certified public accountant and assistant administrator of St. Mary's Hospital and Medical Center, San Francisco, was employed in May 1969 as vice president for financial affairs. Many changes were made, but a cash flow deficit of $131,000 was still evident in November 1969 and the hospital was heavily overdrawn at Wachovia Bank. The bank had faith that the situation could be corrected and allowed the hospital to borrow $450,000 from the Medical Foundation[2] of the medical school and hospital to construct a 14-bed coronary care center that was urgently needed. This was approved on the condition that the unit be treated separately from the financial standpoint and that any surplus be returned to pay off the loan. Although Mr. Held initiated a number of important advances, such as a basic hospital information system, his management style led to conflicts and he resigned.

Mr. John Lynch, associate administrator of the Kansas City Research Hospital, was employed as executive vice president in October 1970. He had a masters degree in business administration, four years of management experience at U.S. Steel before entering the health field and was well-versed in hospital systems and finance. A series of meetings with a special committee on hospital finance, chaired by Mr. Stokes, was initiated in December and included representatives of the medical school. The purpose was to develop a comprehensive program to correct the fiscal problem. Twenty-seven possible courses of action were developed. It was decided that only those that would not jeopardize either the quality of medical care or public relations would be implemented. Seven options met these criteria. They were implemented and resulted in a remarkable turn-around in hospital finances over the next several years. The results were so convincing that the institution was able to qualify for a Federal Housing Administration guaranteed loan subsidy and obtain a $11-million loan from the North Carolina Teachers Pension Fund to meet a shortfall in funds for its portion of the medical center development program, the paramedical school, and start-up expenditures required for the opening of beds in the Reynolds Tower.

One of the elements of the action program necessitated the phasing out of the hospital diploma school of nursing. Though this was traumatic for many of its loyal alumni, it was apparent that traditional three-year nursing schools were losing their appeal to high school seniors and their justification for existence. The costs of operation were borne primarily by patients (approximately $750,000 per year at Baptist Hospital), and required increases in classroom studies had sharply reduced patient care services of students. Furthermore, baccalaureate schools of nursing would not give credit to diploma students who wished to transfer to a degree program. The last class of diploma nursing students graduated in 1974. To offset this loss, Forsyth Technical Institute agreed to initiate an associate degree program in nursing and take over allied health programs in inhalation therapy, nuclear medicine technology and radiation technology. This was done jointly with Forsyth Memorial Hospital, which also phased out its diploma nursing school at that time. A grant from the Kate Bitting Reynolds Health Care Trust provided funds for planning and the operation of these programs during the initial year, as required before the institute was eligible for operating funds from the state. Baptist Hospital gave space in the paramedical school building for these programs and served, with Forsyth Memorial Hospital, as a clinical training site for the students.

Wake Forest Gains University Status

On June 18, 1967, the month before the retirement of President Tribble, the trustees declared Wake Forest a university. Tribble was succeeded on July 1 of that year by Dr. James Ralph Scales, an educator and political scientist who had served as president of Oklahoma Baptist University (1961-1964) and more recently as professor of political science and dean of arts and sciences at Oklahoma State University (1965-1967). He brought with him Gene Lucas, a very astute academic administrator, as vice president for business and finance. Thus began an era which focused on strengthening the university and adding very significantly to its quality and national prominence. It began also a relationship between the administration of the university and the medical school that was both congenial and very supportive. Scales quickly insisted that the first priority in university fund raising was the successful completion of the medical center development program and promptly discontinued plans for the $72 million university campaign that had been proposed by Dr. Tribble. He further believed that more funds could be raised through separate but coordinated development efforts at the medical center and university. The principles for this coordination were carefully outlined in a document which has since become known as "the treaty of 1967."

Coy Carpenter also retired on July 1, 1967 as vice president of medical affairs after 41 years of dedicated service to Wake Forest medicine, and the title of vice president was added to the deanship of the medical school. Dr. Carpenter was named vice president emeritus for health affairs. He died of another heart attack at age 71 on November 7, 1971. Subsequently the medical school library was designated the Coy C. Carpenter Library in his memory.

Program Development at the Medical School

During the latter half of 1967, several important grants were made to the medical school which delayed somewhat the impact of inflation on the operating budget. In recognition of the excellence of the educational and research programs developed by Dr. James F. Toole and his associates, the school was awarded in national competition $600,000 to establish the Walter C. Teagle endowed professorship in Neurology. Dr. Toole, who had been on sabbatical during this time, was named the first recipient of this chair. A five-year grant of $1,780,000 from the NIH was awarded to establish a six-bed general clinical research unit through the efforts of Dr. Richard L. Burt. Dr. Charles L. Spurr and Dr. I. Meschan received a four-year grant of $468,000 to establish a multidisciplinary cancer training program. Though crucial to the programs of academic medical centers, foundations rarely make funds available to strengthen library holdings. A grant of $95,000 from the Markle Foundation for this purpose was particularly welcome at this time.

A most important development occurred in the behavioral sciences. In a reevaluation of the course in preventive medicine, it was recognized that most physicians and faculty members were poorly prepared to deal with patients who had problems related to marriage and human sexuality. In 1956 Mrs. Ethel Nash, a British-trained specialist in this area, was asked to give several lectures on the subject to second-year medical students. She was so well received that she was asked to join the faculty on a part-time basis and expand her teaching and initiate limited consultation services in her specialty. This came to the attention of Frank Lock, who asked her to extend her teaching to residents in obstetrics and gynecology. Through this association both Lock and Nash felt this relevant program in the behavioral sciences should be strengthened. With a five-year grant of $250,000 from the Mary Reynolds Babcock Foundation serving as core support, Lock attracted Dr. Clark Vincent to his department in August 1964. Vincent, a sociologist with a strong research background, had been serving as chief of the Social Sciences Section and chief of the Training Branch, National Institute of Mental Health. He with Mrs. Nash established a training and research program in marital life and sex education at the medical school. This pioneering effort quickly achieved national attention. Grants from the Ford Foundation of $370,000 and the Commonwealth Fund of $120,000 allowed a major expansion of the program, which emphasized research and the training of teachers for other medical schools in family planning, marriage and human sexuality. To give proper representation to this important multidisciplinary effort, it was reorganized as the Behavioral Sciences Center in 1965 with the director, Dr. Vincent, reporting directly to the dean. There is no question that Drs. Vincent and Lock made a major contribution to medical education nationally through these efforts.

Also at this time, the three North Carolina medical schools, jointly with the North Carolina Medical Society, formed the Association for the North Carolina Regional Medical Program. The association was awarded a planning grant of $436,000 under Public Law 89-239 (Heart Disease, Cancer and Stroke) to develop continuing education programs for physicians and allied health personnel through cooperative arrangements with community hospitals. Dr. Marc J. Musser, medical director of the Veterans Administration, was employed as the first executive director. Dr. Louis deS. Shaffner, professor of Surgery, served as director of this important outreach program for the Bowman Gray School of Medicine. In 1968 the association was awarded a three-year operational grant of $2.3 million for core staff and programs. For the first time the schools had funds to mount a major effort in continuing medical education. The history and accomplishments of the North Carolina Regional Medical Program, which terminated in 1975, were well documented by Ben F. Weaver, the last executive director.[3]

Several administrative changes also occurred during this time. After 25 years of service as chairman of obstetrics-gynecology, Dr. Lock requested relief from his administrative duties, and Dr. Richard L. Burt was elected to replace him in October 1966. Lock had been a major force in the development of the school, had achieved national recognition through his research on measles and pregnancy, and through his efforts in behavioral medicine and, uniquely, had served as president of the three major national societies in his specialty.

Dr. Howard H. Bradshaw, who had served as chairman of the Department of Surgery since the beginning of the four-year school, announced in September 1967 that he wished to retire. During the difficult years, "Brad" had built a strong department with very limited financial support from the school, a department which gained broad recognition from the excellence of its residency training, research and clinical programs. His strong leadership, high professional standards and ready willingness to place the institution first during difficult times, contributed much to the survival and reputation of the medical center. Fortunately, an outstanding and highly respected member of his department, Dr. Richard T. Myers, accepted the chairmanship of surgery in July 1968. Myers, a graduate of the University of Pennsylvania School of Medicine, had joined the faculty in 1950 following residency training under Bradshaw. Because of his professional skill and sound judgment, he was known among his peers as the "surgeon's surgeon." This was a time when surgical subspecialties in many medical schools were demanding department status. With remarkable leadership and diplomacy, Myers aborted such a development at Bowman Gray by promptly forming a surgical council made up of the heads of the surgical sections. This mechanism for academic and professional policy discussions and communications contributed much to foster the continued unification and balanced growth of the department. Throughout his long tenure as chairman, Myers' contributions to the center extended far beyond his department, in the areas of policy, planning and community relations.

After the death of Dr. LeRoy Crandell, Dr. Thomas Irving from the University of Kansas Medical Center was selected to head the Section of Anesthesiology in July 1967. Following a major expansion in staff, the development of high quality programs and a strong recommendation from the Department of Surgery, the section was elevated to full departmental status on February 1, 1969.

At this time the paramedical school building was under construction. Pressures were growing nationally for medical schools to help improve the training of allied health personnel and to develop new ways to increase the productivity of physicians. It was agreed jointly by the hospital and medical school that the fragmented training programs then existing, with the exception of diploma nursing and pastoral care, should be consolidated in a Division of Allied Health Science with a director and a core of full-time faculty. This division was to explore also the possible development of new types of personnel and improved methods of teaching. Dr. Leland Powers, who was associate director of the Association of American Medical Colleges and who formerly had developed a school for the training of allied health personnel at the American University of Beirut, was contacted and agreed to accept the challenge as director of this new division, effective July 1, 1968. He was familiar with the school and had helped Dr. Meads in reorienting the teaching program in preventive medicine at Bowman Gray in 1951, when he served as chairman of that department at the University of Washington School of Medicine in Seattle. Powers brought his unique educational and administrative experience and skills to the development of the new division, which allowed the medical center to make important contributions to allied health education and training. Among these was the development of the second program in the country for physician assistants, which began in 1969; and the introduction of self-instructional aids to the curriculum which later were widely used by other institutions.

A very welcomed addition to the library occurred in 1967 with the appointment of Mrs. Erika Love as head librarian. She had served since 1958 in this position at the Carter Memorial Library of the Indiana University Medical Center, and changed the orientation of Bowman Gray's library from a primarily custodial operation to a dynamic public service resource. The collection was reclassified in accord with the National Library of Medicine system and an intensive training program for the staff was initiated.

As mentioned previously, an important element in the planning of the Medical Center Development program was the opportunity to design facilities to allow needed changes in curriculum, the introduction of new teaching methods, and the expansion of educational support services. Nationally, concerns related to the process of medical education were focusing on three areas: 1) coping with the rapidly expanding body of scientific knowledge, 2) selecting materials from the behavioral sciences that were relevant to medical education and 3) refining ways to demonstrate to students continuing comprehensive care in university teaching hospitals that were increasingly stressing episodic, disease-oriented patient care. The Committee on Medical Education, reorganized in 1966 for these purposes, had made important contributions to the facilities planning process. The committee presented a general proposal for curriculum revision at another three-day faculty retreat in Roanoke, Virginia in

June 1968. Discussions were prefaced by an overview of the "crisis" in medical education and medical services and their overriding implications for the education of future physicians. The general proposals were accepted and the revised curriculum was phased in beginning with the entering class of 1969, which was also able to occupy the new medical school facilities of the Hanes Building and Babcock Auditorium. Dr. Robert L. Tuttle had given excellent leadership to this entire process and, again, the faculty retreat greatly assisted in educating the faculty on the rapidly changing environment of medicine and in helping to facilitate curriculum change.

The medical school and the community felt a sense of great loss with the death of Bowman Gray, Jr. in 1969. Despite the handicap of his chronic illness, he maintained a continual interest in the development of the institution and through his will left a significant bequest to its endowment.

The Emerging National Paradox

By June 1968 it was apparent that many academic centers in this country would soon be experiencing major financial problems. The number of U.S. troops in Vietnam was escalating rapidly, inflation continued at eight to ten percent per year and major cut-backs were being made in funds for federal domestic programs, including biomedical research and training grants. Many of the grants included partial salary support for faculty and stipends for graduate students and postdoctoral fellows. At this time faculty salary support from such grants at Bowman Gray amounted to more than $1 million a year. This problem was compounded because the rapidly rising cost of construction had forced postponement of the endowment phase of the Medical Center Development program, and operating costs were expected to increase very significantly with the occupancy of new medical school facilities in September 1969.

Nationally, these events resulted in a paradox. While inflation and cut-backs in federal funds were creating severe financial problems for medical schools and their teaching hospitals, pressures were mounting for these academic medical centers to produce more health manpower, restructure their educational programs, deliver more patient services, and become more involved in helping to solve health problems in their communities and regions.

During 1968, a series of conferences sponsored by foundations and government resulted in the unanimous opinion that academic medical centers lacked a stable financial base; that they could not effectively participate in extramural programs; and that, because of inflation, a reduction in the quality of their programs was possible soon. A number of private schools had begun liquidating endowment to maintain their programs. As a result, several states began capitation programs for their private medical schools. The Congress enacted legislation to assist health professional schools through special improvement grants and student financial aid.

In anticipation of these problems at Bowman Gray, an action plan was developed after extensive discussions with the Faculty Executive Council. First, a policy was established whereby the medical school would participate in new programs and outreach activities only to the extent they would not jeopardize the quality of its core programs of education, research and patient care. Secondly, to meet projected financial requirements for the year beginning July 1, 1969, a multisource approach was developed and approved by President Scales. It was projected that $660,000 in new income was needed by July 1969 for faculty salaries, increased maintenance costs and augmentation of the supporting staff. This goal was achieved and financial crisis averted by a modest tuition increase, successful competition for a federal special improvement grant, an agreement by the clinical faculty that 75 percent of Medicare and Medicaid fees collected on staff patients should be used for general institutional purposes, the phasing in of university support for graduate student stipends, an intensive campaign to increase alumni annual giving and the initiation of state capitation for North Carolina students at Bowman Gray and Duke Medical Schools—a story in itself. The alumni response after six regional meetings to explain candidly the school's financial difficulty was very gratifying, and set a pattern for annual operational support, as previous giving had been directed primarily for construction programs. The effort won the 1970 national Alumni Giving Incentive Award among professional schools, and took third place among all colleges and universities in that year.

In addition to a temporary freeze on budgeted unfilled positions, another internal cost-saving adjustment should be mentioned at this time. Excessively stringent federal guidelines had forced the architect to design a system in the new Hanes Building that exhausted all heat and air conditioning to the outside, without any internal turnover. After the buildings had been given final federal inspection and approval,

Mr. George Jones, the long-time head of the school's department of engineering and maintenance, told the dean that, if he would give him $15,000 without asking any questions, he would save the school thousands of dollars each year in utility costs. Recognizing the uniquely creative abilities of Jones, this was approved. In short order, with valves and cross connections, air circulation to the outside was reduced to meet the usual codes for such buildings, and major savings in utility costs were achieved.

State Financial Aid to Increase Opportunities for
North Carolinians to Study Medicine (IMEO Program)

In the late 1960s, Duke and the University of North Carolina Schools of Medicine were projecting financial problems also, due to continuing inflation and cutbacks in federal grants. Like Bowman Gray they were exploring ways to help correct the shortage of physicians in the state if reasonable financial stability of the institutions could be achieved. The three deans had discussed these problems together and with the leadership of the State Medical Society on a number of occasions, particularly after the North Carolina General Assembly had authorized conditionally the development of a two-year medical school at East Carolina University in 1965 and again in 1967. During the 1967 session, the General Assembly directed the legislative research commission "to study ways and means of providing more doctors for small towns and rural areas with the purpose of recommending legislation toward that end." A sub-committee chaired by Hugh S. Johnson, Jr. of Duplin County was appointed to carry out this mission. A public hearing was held in January 1968, and the deans of the two private schools, at the request of the committee, testified on the severe financial problems of medical schools, and expressed a desire to help in alleviating the shortage of physicians within the state if support could be made available through some form of financial subsidy similar to that in several other states. At a second public hearing in October 1968 the three deans testified again and indicated that financial problems had greatly intensified, pointing to a number of medical schools that were deficit financing or liquidating endowments in order to survive, and outlining the specific financial difficulties at their respective institutions. The presentation received wide media attention throughout the state which was corroborated by similar attention given to this country-wide problem in a variety of national publications. In conversations with Dr. Isaac Taylor, dean of the University of North Carolina School of Medicine, the deans of the two private schools agreed to place first priority for state funding on the university's plan to request $11 million to expand its facilities to allow class size enlargement. In return, Taylor agreed that, although he could not speak for state subsidy for the private schools, he would not speak against it.

During the October hearing, Mr. Hugh Johnson invited the Bowman Gray and Duke Medical Schools to submit a proposal for state aid. As Bowman Gray had just completed a detailed cost study indicating that the pedagogic cost of medical education at that institution was $4,328 per student per year, William Anlyan, dean of the Duke Medical School, agreed that this was a defensible level of financial support to request after subtracting tuition at the University of North Carolina which was $700 per year at that time. We believed this approach would be an incentive also for the private schools to admit more North Carolinians and, with the proposed expansion at the university, was a far quicker and cheaper way to produce more physicians for the state than to build a new medical school.

At this point a number of complex political issues emerged. The mission of the legislative subcommittee was to get more doctors into rural areas. The issue of licensing osteopaths in North Carolina arose favorably within the committee. Senator Robert Morgan tentatively proposed that a major portion of any state subsidy be based on the number of graduates from the private schools that chose family medicine and committed themselves to practice in rural areas. The two deans promptly turned down this proposal as coercive and unacceptable. At this point, the State Board of Higher Education was asked to assist the legislative subcommittee on this entire matter.

The three deans met with the chairman of this board, Watts Hill, Jr., and Cameron West, its executive director. It was quickly evident that both viewed the situation in the context of higher education and favored state financial support for private universities and colleges in North Carolina in order to use existing resources in an optimal manner. To achieve this goal they thought the place to start from the political standpoint would be the two private medical schools. Their assessment was that the legislative subcommittee would like to use the plight of the medical schools to direct our efforts strongly toward producing family practitioners for rural areas. Therefore, they felt the best approach would be the direct introduction of a bill in the legislature by friends of the two institutions. Further, they thought that in such legislation we should limit the request to operational funds based only on the number of North Carolina students, using our proposed level of capitation per student. To help justify such a request, they noted the precedent set in providing capitation payments for black North Carolinians who attended Meharry Medical School in Tennessee through a compact with the Southern Regional Education Board. To bypass issues of church and state, capitation would be in the form of a contract with the schools for services rendered and not a direct subsidy.

The three deans testified before the full Board of Higher Education in December 1968, a month before the beginning of the session of the General Assembly. The board established a Committee on the Shortage of Doctors in North Carolina, chaired by W.C. (Buck) Harris of Raleigh, Dr. Hubert M. Poteat of Smithfield and Dr. Isaac H. Miller, president of Bennett College, Greensboro, to develop recommendations.

In the meantime, the deans of Bowman Gray and Duke kept Dr. George Paschal, Jr., then president of the State Medical Society, abreast of the rapidly moving events and received from him valuable counsel and support. They conferred with the governor, lieutenant governor, speaker of the house and key members of the legislature, each time receiving sympathetic or direct support for our proposal. Alumni of the two private schools who were personal physicians of members of the legislature were mobilized and given written background material to use on our behalf. Medical students who were residents of North Carolina were encouraged to contact their legislative representatives. To allay any concerns of the Baptist constituency, Editor Marse Grant agreed to publish in the *Biblical Recorder* a very supportive editorial from the *Winston-Salem Journal*. It was followed by his comment that the medical schools' participation in the program in no way compromised the doctrine of separation of church and state.

The report of the Board of Higher Education was released to the public in March 1969.[4] As agreed, first priority was given to funds to expand the University of North Carolina School of Medicine as this item had not appeared in the governor's budget. The second priority was a "contract for services" with Bowman Gray and Duke which would begin by providing $3,250 for each North Carolina student enrolled in the first-year class in the fall of 1969. Of this amount, $1,000 would go toward a reduction of tuition to decrease the financial differential between the state and private medical schools. The remainder was to be used for instructional purposes. It was stressed that these two priorities reflected the quickest way to help correct the shortage of physicians in the state. As for the proposed new medical school at East Carolina University, continued study was recommended.

In April 1969, Hugh Johnson accepted the logic in this approach and introduced a bill embodying these recommendations in the House, and John T. Henley introduced a companion bill in the Senate. A segment of the Academy of General Practice wrote letters of objection as the legislation did not force the schools to train family physicians for rural areas. At the same time, supporters of the East Carolina University Medical School, who had been biding their time, introduced legislation to increase support for the proposed two-year medical school. Despite these swirling political issues, the General Assembly approved state aid for Bowman Gray and Duke at the level of $2,500 per North Carolina student beginning with those admitted in the fall of 1969. Of that sum, $250 was to go toward tuition reduction.[5] At the same time, $10 million was appropriated for the expansion program at the University of North Carolina School of Medicine. Perhaps prophetic of the events leading up to this action, seed money was approved also for the establishment of a state zoo.

This, of course, did not end the matter, as the state appropriation for the private schools came from a supplement to the general budget and covered only the next biennium.

Both medical schools responded in good faith beyond the maximum expected by the general assembly, as shown below:

	Entering Class Size	
	1966-1969 Average	1970-1971
Bowman Gray School of Medicine Total (NC Residents)	61 (24)	76 (40)
Duke University School of Medicine Total (NC Residents)	86 (9)	104 (26)
Total	147 (33)	180 (66)

This good faith response in creating 33 additional first-year places for North Carolinians, as the result of a partial cost of education grant and no capital expenditures by the state, impressed members of the 1971 General Assembly. In addition, in keeping with trends at other medical schools, Bowman Gray had reorganized preventive medicine as a Department of Community Medicine in May 1970. Chaired by Donald M. Hayes, the department oversaw the community preceptorship rotations for medical students that gave them a unique insight into primary patient care and community health care resources. Our primary objective during the 1971 session in Raleigh was to stabilize the contract program and improve the tuition-remission feature. Obviously the amount of funds received by each school was growing as credit was received for each North Carolina student that progressed through the curriculum. These objectives were accomplished by legislation which provided "continuing support" rather than on a biennial basis and by an increase in the tuition-remission feature to $500 per student per year. To accomplish the latter it was agreed that the tuition funds would be pooled and awarded to North Carolina students on the basis of need up to $1,500 per year.

In 1971 the General Assembly enacted legislation restructuring higher education in North Carolina by forming a 16-campus University of North Carolina system and creating a 35-member board of governors to supervise it, which replaced the State Board of Higher Education. Capitation funds for the private medical schools became part of the budget of this new board under Dr. William C. Friday, who was elected president of the system. This was indeed fortunate, as President Friday was supportive of the program and was responsible for its expansion at a later date. As such, the deans now dealt directly with Dr. Friday and his board, which served as a buffer between the private schools and the general assembly. Soon after, the private colleges and universities as a group sought state capitation support for North Carolinians in their undergraduate programs. This was approved by the General Assembly in 1975.

Medical Center Involvement in Community Health Planning

One additional dimension was added to the complex array of challenges that emerged during the late 1960s. In 1965, as noted before, the Congress had enacted the Partnership for Health Act to encourage comprehensive health planning at the state and local levels. This included health manpower, facilities and services. This legislation marked the beginning of national concern for the organization and delivery of health care and an effort to promote the rational use of health resources.

111

During 1965–1966, the Citizens Planning Council of Forsyth County formed a Joint Health Planning Committee with the Urban Coalition and conducted a community health survey. The study was headed by Morris Weisner, an executive of R.J. Reynolds Tobacco Company. His committee was made up almost entirely of laymen representing major corporate contributors to these two organizations. The report described a number of problems and indicated that the goal of the county should be to develop a unified and coordinated system of health care services which would assure every citizen equal access to basic medical care of good quality at the least possible cost. Areas of major concern were health care for the medically indigent, mental health services and the status of the Kate B. Reynolds Memorial Hospital that served predominantly the black population of east Winston-Salem. The study added impetus for the construction, near the old facility, of the new 250-bed Reynolds Memorial Hospital, which opened in January 1970.

In 1968, in anticipation of this new facility, a cooperative arrangement was developed between the medical school and the Reynolds Hospital staff which was funded by a three-year grant of $600,000 from the Z. Smith Reynolds Foundation. This allowed the recruitment of full-time black physicians who served as chiefs of service for pediatrics, surgery, medicine and obstetrics-gynecology. They were given faculty appointments at the medical school, and medical student and house staff rotations were planned at Reynolds Hospital while additional clinical faculty conducted conferences and served in a consulting capacity. The objective was to strengthen the hospital staff, to encourage more black physicians to move into the community, and to have the institution serve more effectively as back-up for a new associated comprehensive family care clinic. That clinic was funded by the United States Public Health Service as a cooperative effort between the Experiment in Self-Reliance and the Office of Equal Opportunity. Dr. David Savitz, a young and energetic public health service officer, was assigned to organize and direct the clinic. Access to medical care and its quality improved significantly; however, the clinic became relatively isolated from the mainstream of medicine in the community. Student and house staff rotations were limited, as early on the new chiefs of staff made it quite clear that the Reynolds Foundation program and the responsibility for carrying it out were theirs, and the major objective was to develop a first-class community hospital.

112

Mr. C. Sebastian Sommer, executive director of the Winston-Salem Foundation, became chairman of the Citizen's Planning Council and believed greater input from the medical community was needed if the goals of the Weisner study were to be achieved. In the spring of 1969 he arranged an informal meeting at a lakeside cabin in the country with Harold Koach, administrator of the Forsyth Memorial Hospital, David Savitz, and the dean of the medical school. One of the results of that meeting was the acceptance of the dean's recommendation to establish a Professional Conference Group, representing the medical leadership of the community. A similar group had been formed in January 1969 at the state level, in order to assure proper medical input into statewide policy in the area of health planning. It was agreed that the local group would serve in an advisory capacity to the Citizen's Planning Council.

The first meeting of the Professional Conference Group was held in June 1969 at Graylyn. Those attending were Sebastian Sommer; Reid Bahnson, president of the Forsyth County Medical Society; Richard Sherrill, president of the Twin City Medical Society; the chiefs of staff of the three hospitals, Joseph Gordon, Joyce Reynolds and Eben Alexander; hospital administrators Harold Koach and Reid Holmes; James Finger, public health officer; and David Savitz. Dr. Meads served as moderator.

The Professional Conference Group met regularly discussing the various aspects of community health problems, access to health care, and approaches to health planning. In December 1969 a memorandum was sent to the boards of the Citizen's Planning Council and the Urban Coalition from this group and the Joint Health Planning Committee, urging the establishment of a community comprehensive health planning organization and recommending principles of organization, functions and staff support. This action in part was precipitated by a recent Bureau of Budget Circular A-95 that made it clear that community, regional and state health planning agencies must be established if such areas were to be eligible for federal grants for a variety of health care construction and service programs. The proposal was endorsed by the hospitals and medical societies under a resolution indicating that they would recognize such an organization as the sole community health planning agency and would be willing to participate and share information necessary for its proper function. The Forsyth Health Planning Council was established in September 1970 and received financial support from a number of corporations and businesses within the community. Regional and statewide counterparts rapidly followed.

The new Health Planning Council, with input from the Professional Conference Group, served as the catalyst for major changes in the health care system in Forsyth County that occurred over the next several years. Studies resulted initially in the consolidation of allied health manpower training at Forsyth Technical Institute as mentioned previously, and the consolidation of Reynolds and Forsyth Memorial Hospitals under an independent hospital authority. In June 1971 a task force on improvement in medical care was established by the council and chaired by Linwood Davis, a respected lawyer in Winston-Salem. Its purpose was to study the overall medical care system and make recommendations for improvement in the quality and accessibility of medical care and for containing its costs. All institutions and programs within the county were to be considered with the exception of mental health, which was under study by another group. The results had a major impact on medical services in the community, including the medical center, and on the future of Reynolds Hospital. This hospital had an average occupancy rate of 50 percent and was operating at a significant deficit, requiring a subsidy from the county each year. The task force pointed up the lack of availability of primary medical care and the inappropriate use of emergency rooms for this purpose; deficits in maternal and child care that were reflected in high rates of maternal and infant mortality; the inappropriate use of some of the existing hospital beds; continued low occupancy rate at Reynolds Hospital; health manpower shortages; and inadequate financing for the care of the medically indigent. After considerable public and professional discussion, studies by an outside consultant, and several informal retreats away from the city involving the medical leadership and key county commissioners, all of the major recommendations of the task force were implemented. Dr. Joseph Gordon and Commissioner C.C. Ross deserve tremendous credit for their leadership within the black community in making this possible. Harold Koach gave similar leadership at Forsyth Memorial Hospital. The ultimate results were that:

Reynolds Hospital was phased out as a general hospital in 1973. This was preceded by a unification of its professional staff with that of Forsyth Memorial to assure reciprocal admitting privileges. Fair treatment was assured for Reynolds Hospital employees through transfer of seniority and employment in the other two hospitals.

A portion of Reynolds Hospital was converted and used to develop a major outpatient primary care center, which later was staffed by Bowman Gray faculty under contract with the county and used also as a site for medical student and house staff training.

Inpatient obstetrical care for all patients was consolidated at Forsyth Memorial, including obstetrical anesthesia and neonatal intensive care. The unit is staffed by Bowman Gray faculty and community physicians, thus eliminating unnecessary duplication and allowing all patients access to excellent maternal and neonatal care.

The treatment of nonsurgical inpatient pediatric and highly specialized cancer patients was consolidated at Baptist Hospital.

All services of the medical center were affiliated with Forsyth Memorial Hospital, which became an important extension of the teaching programs of the medical center and, as will be seen, allowed a further expansion in the medical student body and in the residency programs.

All of these changes achieved an improvement in the quality and accessibility of medical care, reduced unnecessary duplication and fragmentation of services, and established a major ambulatory care center in a location of greatest need. Unfortunately, the extensive discussions of the mental health task force did not materialize into acceptable recommendations and the task force was disbanded.

Retrospect

The variety of complex social, economic and political issues that emerged in the late 1960s to challenge academic medical centers was unprecedented. The confluence of inflation, sharp cut-backs in federal support for research and research training, and mounting pressures to help solve community and regional health care problems had a particularly devastating impact on many private institutions. Bowman Gray and Baptist Hospital faced major threats to their financial stability and their ongoing facilities expansion program. At the same time the center was engaged in important but highly sensitive changes in the community health care system, in the implementation of a major revision in curriculum, in salvaging a graduate program hard hit by losses in federal training grants, and in direct involvement for the first time in the state political arena.

Again, as in the past, problems were resolved through the

115

coordinated efforts of many who placed highest priority on the survival of the medical center. Plans and policy emerged through frank and candid discussions in the Faculty Executive Council. Internally, Eben Alexander as chief of Professional Services oversaw the maintenance of the quality of patient care. Nash Herndon, as associate dean for Research Development, skillfully negotiated mandated cutbacks in federal grants to protect, where possible, faculty salary support. Robert Tuttle guided curriculum change and its implementation until January 1970 when he accepted the position of academic dean, and later dean, of the newly developing University of Texas Health Sciences Center at Houston. Dick Janeway was called on to implement the new clinical curriculum and readily demonstrated his leadership ability in this complex area. Douglas Maynard supervised both admissions and student affairs exceptionally well after Bob Tuttle left the institution; and Emery Miller, as associate dean, reorganized and strengthened the expanding program of continuing education. Harry Parker, until his cerebrovascular accident in March 1970, valiantly maintained a tight but balanced budget, despite cries of "scrooge" from the few uninitiated who attempted to bypass the system. It was truly a team approach. Katherine Davis, assistant to the dean, in her quiet, experienced and resourceful way served as the glue to keep things together during the many occasions that demanded the dean's time outside of the institution. One must pause in this story to pay tribute also to the support given by President Scales; and the outstanding assistance and vigorous trustee leadership of Colin Stokes in helping to resolve the hospital financial crisis. Very special appreciation is due also to John Watlington who became chairman of the Board of Visitors in 1969, succeeding Albert Butler. Mr. Watlington's valuable advice and counsel, and the untold hours he gave to the successful completion of the Medical Center Development program campaign with Tom Davis and other members of the Board of Visitors during these difficult times was unparalleled.

As a result of these combined efforts, the medical school was given full accreditation by the Liaison Committee on Medical Education as the result of a site visit in February 1971. It was rewarding to all concerned that the report was highly complimentary of the development of faculty, facilities and curriculum that had occurred since the last accreditation in 1963.

The Medical Center before the Development Program (circa 1960)

Albert L. Butler, Jr.

John F. Watlington, Jr.

J. Ralph Scales

Thomas H. Davis

Ralph P. Hanes

Colin Stokes

Gordon Hanes

Lost to Progress
Implosion of the old power plant 1969

The Medical Center (1977) before
the Challenge Program

The Medical Center Board of Directors 1976
Standing, left to right: E. Lawrence Davis, III, Dr. George W. Paschal, Jr., J. Edwin
Collette, Robert Forney, Rev. R. F. Smith, Dr. J. Donald Bradsher, Dr. Ernest Stines,
Dr. Thomas D. Long, Francis E. Garvin. Seated, left to right: Dr. Jesse Chapman,
Joyce Warren, Dr. Mary L. Morris, Polly L. Blackwell, E. J. Prevatte.
Not present: A. H. Field, Leon L. Rice, Jr., Dr. Eben Alexander, Jr.

References and Notes

1. Annual of the Baptist Convention of North Carolina, 1968, pp. 167–168.
2. For a description of the Medical Foundation see Supplement 1.
3. Weaver, Ben F., North Carolina Regional Medical Program, July 1975.
4. Report of Committee on Shortages of Doctors in North Carolina. Special Report 2-69 (March 1969), North Carolina Board of Higher Education, Raleigh, North Carolina.
5. An Act to Provide Financial Assistance for the Education of North Carolinians at The Medical Schools of Duke University and Wake Forest University (House Bill 653) approved July 2, 1969.

CHAPTER VII

The Beginning of a New Era
—the 1970's

By 1971 the acute financial crisis of Baptist Hospital and the medical school had been resolved and both institutions could foresee a period of reasonable financial stability. Through this difficult period, both had refused to abandon high quality for expediency in order to solve their problems.

John Lynch Appointed Chief Executive Officer of the Hospital

For the year 1971, Baptist Hospital had operating expenditures of $17,350,000, including depreciation, and a net income of $1,389,400, which was used to erase the 1970 deficit, to meet payments on long-term debt and to allow the purchase of the most urgent capital needs.[1] John Lynch, who had served as executive vice president since October 1970, was designated chief executive officer in April 1972, and Reid Holmes retained the title of president until his official retirement in 1974. The appointment of Lynch to this position reflected the expertise and leadership he brought to the hospital. It represented also a trend in the larger institutions to seek chief executives with strong management, rather than solely administrative, experience.

The new 14-bed coronary care unit opened in October 1971, and the Z. Smith Reynolds Foundation Tower was scheduled for occupancy at the end of 1972, which would bring total bed capacity to 672. Inflation and more restrictive safety codes had forced a review of plans to renovate older hospital and outpatient facilities for the expansion of ambulatory and emergency services. It was determined that, for the same cost and with major gains in program efficiency and flexibility, a new facility could be constructed adjacent to the Reynolds Tower. The original plans were abandoned and in April 1972 construction was initiated on the new 42,000-square-foot two-story ambulatory care building which included space for clinics, a modern emergency room and enlarged facilities for the rapidly expanding radiation oncology program.

By the time this decision was made the overall cost of the Medical Center Development program, which now included the costs of the Allied Health School Building, had increased to $40.8 million. The remaining funds needed were covered by the successful Phase II campaign and, in part, by the FHA-subsidized loan obtained by the hospital. At the end of the two-phased campaign $13,409,478 had been obtained from federal sources and $20,133,911 had been subscribed from private sources.

New facilities had changed the major entrance of patient care facilities from the east to the west, and required reorientation of parking facilities. The hospital was constructing public facilities in front of the Reynolds Tower, but was unable to purchase enough land across Hawthorne Road to the east for employee parking because of the high prices being asked by absentee property owners. The problem was solved with the help of Mr. John Gold, the city manager. Through the issuance of bonds and the power of eminent domain, the city purchased most of the block across Hawthorne Road and constructed parking facilities. On completion, the hospital transferred the operation of their public parking facilities to the city; and hospital employees used the new city-owned parking area. Public parking fees were used to meet city payments on the bonds. There was no transfer of ownership of properties. This cooperation between the city and a private institution was based on the precedent set in the downtown areas that the city could provide public parking where demands justified it. The venture turned out to be a very profitable one for the city, as net revenues from public parking at the medical center soon helped to meet deficits incurred by the city in several of its other parking facilities.

The introduction of modern management systems, the faculty commitment to an efficient utilization of beds, and the action program noted previously had been instrumental in resolving the immediate financial problems of Baptist Hospital. The goal ahead was to achieve financial stability by building reserve funds to allow not only a catch-up in technology but also to initiate new programs and insure that the center could be maintained at the forefront of advances in patient care. Contributing to this objective was the fact that funded depreciation in the immediate years ahead could build rapidly as a reserve because new facilities and equipment had been purchased by funds raised primarily through the Medical Center Development program and not through borrowing. This, plus the projected increased utilization of the hospital and the management efficiencies, augured well for the achievement of this objective.

Also by 1971, the medical school had solved its immediate financial problems through its action program that had generated new income from federal special improvement grants, increased alumni giving, the state aid program, professional income from staff medical services, and beginning support by the university for graduate students in the basic medical sciences. These funds met projected deficits and allowed a modest expansion in the full-time faculty from 150 to 176, as required for class expansion, the new curriculum and associated support services. Expenditures for the year 1970–1971 totaled $11,683,505 and $951,000 had been accumulated as an institutional reserve fund. State aid and support for graduate students were scheduled to increase annually during the next several years, as was medical service income when the new hospital beds under construction became available. The Comprehensive Health Manpower Training Act of 1971 promised direct operational support for new and expanding health professions schools and increased student aid. All pointed to a brighter fiscal future for the institution in the years ahead.

Mr. Harry Parker was unable to return to the medical school as chief financial officer after his cerebrovascular accident. He was replaced by Mr. Warren Kennedy in October 1971. Kennedy had been serving as chief financial officer of Vanderbilt University medical center and came to Bowman Gray as associate dean of Administration and director of the newly organized Division of Resource Management.

Also at this time the NIH established a new program to fund specialized centers of research (SCOR) in the area of atherosclerosis. The application from Drs. Thomas Clarkson and Hugh B Lofland placed third among all applicant medical schools. They were awarded a five-year grant of $2,977,519 for multidisciplinary research in this field. A large number of existing grants in atherosclerosis research were folded into the new program, mainly from the Departments of Comparative Medicine and Pathology. Drs. Clarkson and Hugh Lofland from the two departments shared the directorship of the SCOR program. Because of the outstanding contributions that the center has made to the better understanding of atherosclerosis, it has received continuing and increasing support from federal and private sources.

Dr. Richard Janeway Elected Dean

Following the departure of Dr. Tuttle, it was agreed that the growing complexity and demands of medical school administration required not only a full-time replacement, but also a separation of the vice presidency and deanship. The Faculty Executive Council as a whole agreed to serve as a search committee and favored an appointment from within the institution if possible. The choice of a new dean was not difficult, as one person stood out as the obvious candidate—Dr. Richard Janeway. Janeway came to Bowman Gray as a resident in neurology in 1965, following two years in the Air Force. He is a graduate of the University of Pennsylvania School of Medicine, where he also took internship and residency training in medicine. He joined the Bowman Gray faculty in 1966, and was selected as a Markle Scholar two years later. In addition to a growing national reputation as a clinician, teacher and investigator in neurology, he had demonstrated exceptional leadership and administrative ability while serving one year as interim chairman of the Department of Neurology during Dr. Toole's sabbatical and thereafter in the implementation of the new curriculum. With the concurrence of the president and trustees, Janeway became the seventh dean of Wake Forest's medical school on July 1, 1971.

Under this new administrative organization as outlined for the Faculty Executive Council in July 1971, the major responsibilities of the dean of the medical school included faculty development, budget, space, curriculum and educational programs. Dr. Meads, vice president for medical affairs, had the primary responsibility for overall institutional policy, planning and development, including public relations, fund raising and relations with the university, government and affiliated hospitals. The close and productive relationship that quickly developed between the dean and vice president was particularly important in view of the increasing demands and opportunities that lay ahead.

The appointment of a new dean was timely, as it allowed him to select and fill a number of important administrative positions that were soon to become vacant due to mandatory retirement from such positions, illness, or other circumstances.

Dr. Harold D. Green, who had served with distinction as chairman of the Department of Physiology since 1945, was replaced by Dr. N. Sheldon Skinner (Emory University School of Medicine) in 1972. Green was a leading voice in the development of the basic medical sciences and had developed outstanding research and doctoral training programs in cardiovascular disease which had long been supported by the National Institutes of Health and a variety of private sources.

Dr. Joseph E. Johnson, III from the University of Florida School of Medicine became chairman of the Department of Medicine in October 1972 when Dr. Ernest H. Yount resigned to return to full-time academic and clinical activities after 20 years in that position. Yount, a Markle Scholar, had been a major stabilizing force at the center during those difficult years. He had developed excellent educational and clinical programs during a time of fiscal constraints, and had contributed immensely to sound center-wide planning and policy formation.

Dr. Richard L. Burt, who had served as chairman of the Department of Obstetrics and Gynecology since Dr. Frank R. Lock gave up that position in 1966, tragically had developed Alzheimer's disease. He was replaced in 1972 by the leading member of the department, Dr. Frank C. Greiss, who was conducting a nationally recognized study on uterine blood flow. Burt was known internationally for his studies on carbohydrate metabolism in pregnancy. As chairman, he gave unselfishly of his time to the initiation of the Ph.D. program at the medical school, to the design of the research wing with Mr. George Jones, and to the development of the inpatient clinical research unit supported by the National Institutes of Health.

Dr. Weston M. Kelsey, who served as chairman of the Department of Pediatrics between 1954 and 1974, was replaced by Dr. Jimmy Simon (University of Texas Medical Branch, Galveston). Kelsey had maintained strong core educational and clinical programs and was a superior teacher. Despite his persistent demand for the highest possible level of excellence, he was beloved by students and faculty alike.

In 1972 Dr. Robert P. ("Moose") Morehead held the longest tenure of any faculty member with Wake Forest medicine. Reaching the age of administrative retirement, he was replaced as chairman of the Department of Pathology in 1973 by an outstanding member of this staff, Dr. Robert W. Prichard. Morehead had served for 27 years as department chairman. A stimulating teacher, and the "right hand" of Coy Carpenter during his deanship, Morehead maintained a large department that rendered an important extramural surgical pathology service to many community hospitals throughout the state. His loyalty to Wake Forest and the medical school was unparalleled. Prichard had worked extensively with Tom Clarkson in the development of atherosclerosis research and the Department of Comparative Medicine. For years he served as editor of the *North Carolina Medical Journal* following the death of Wingate Johnson, and was a major force in the development of the library. He also taught a lively course in the history of medicine.

Mrs. Erika Love, who had made a major contribution to upgrading the library, resigned in the fall of 1971 to become deputy director of the National Library of Medicine. She was replaced in January 1972 by Mr. Michael D. Sprinkle from the University of Kentucky Medical Center. As budgetary limitations eased and space expanded during the 1970s, the library was able to adopt a number of the technical advances being made in library science. A variety of on-line reference services were introduced, and audiovisual and computer-assisted learning resources were rapidly expanded. By the end of the decade the library had developed into a full service operation and, through the Area Health Education Center program, had extended many of these services to community hospitals throughout the region.

Graylyn Becomes a True Asset

The use of Graylyn estate by the medical school for some medically related purpose posed problems from the time of the initial gift by Mrs. Nathalie Gray Bernard in September 1941. Adjacent to the Reynolda estate, Graylyn was located four miles from the medical school. The property had been deeded in parcels over a period of several years to the university for the benefit of the medical school. It represented 22 acres of prime land which included farm buildings, the manor house and associated facilities. The first proposed use as a research institute did not materialize. It had difficulty surviving as a neuropsychiatric hospital between 1947–1958, and then served as a center for children with psychologic, speech and reading problems in association with the Amos Cottage facility for retarded children. The major buildings were not air conditioned, the deteriorating plumbing was British in origin, and the cost of maintaining the buildings and grounds was a continuing problem. These costs were barely offset by rents from apartment units that were developed in the farm buildings and portions of the manor house which were used by faculty and employees of the medical school.

Gordon Gray sensed the problem faced by the medical school and the fact that this magnificent estate built by his father in 1928 could not be preserved under existing conditions. Further, he was fully aware that it had not served its value as a true asset to the school. Mr. Gray initiated conversations with the administration of the school in 1970 and commissioned a study of possible options for the use of Graylyn that included a conference center, a retirement facility and a possible site for the headquarters of R.J. Reynolds Tobacco Company. The last option did not prove feasible; however, the university expressed an interest in exploring other options further.

In early 1973 Mr. Gray proposed that Graylyn be transferred to the university itself and, in return, the medical school would receive $75,000 a year from Triangle Broadcasting Company, later Summit Communications, of which he was a major stockholder. The annual contribution was to discontinue at his death and, through his will, the school would receive $1.5 million to be used as unrestricted endowment. The agreement was approved in March 1973 and, through Mr. Gray's beneficence, Graylyn was turned into a true asset for the medical school and was properly preserved by the university and converted subsequently into a successful executive conference center. Gordon Gray died November 26, 1982, and was the last surviving member of the committee for the Bowman Gray Fund. Throughout his distinguished career in his positions in academic, government and business affairs, his intense interest in the medical school, particularly, since rejoining the Board of Visitors in 1962, was of considerable importance during this period of development.

Under the leadership of Mrs. Barbara L. Hanes, funds were raised to build a new facility to relocate Amos Cottage and the Developmental Evaluation Clinic on the grounds of Forsyth Memorial Hospital. The move occurred in 1975 and assured the continuation of these important regional services under the professional supervision of the Department of Pediatrics.

Medical Center Incorporation—A Compromise Toward Unification

Colin Stokes, as chairman of the hospital trustees between 1968 and 1970, was an active participant in the development and monitoring of the action plan to correct the severe financial problems of the hospital. He had recognized quickly the critical financial and functional interdependence of the hospital and medical school. Just before his term as chairman ended, he recommended to both trustee bodies and the Board of Visitors that a joint committee study this relationship and recommend ways to prevent such a crisis from happening again. This was accepted and committee members were: T. Clyde Collins, Jr. (Chairman), Francis E. Garvin and Curtis Long representing the hospital trustees; Claude McNeill, Jr. and J. Edwin Collette representing the university trustees; Albert L. Butler, Jr. from the Board of Visitors; and Eben Alexander, Jr. who served as the professional staff representative. The committee held a series of meetings with the administrative staffs of each institution and clinical department chairmen. Because of the complexity of the matter, approval was given by the trustees to employ national consultants.[2]

The consultants received extensive background information on each institution and conducted interviews during a five-day period in August 1971 with administration, faculty, President Scales and representatives of the boards of trustees, the Baptist State Convention and local community hospitals. This was followed by a two-day retreat with the joint committee in early October and the presentation of a confidential, written report to the group shortly thereafter.[3] In brief, the report indicated that the purpose of the study was to focus on and define an effective organizational structure that could be responsive to change and representative in its governance. The consultants were convinced that a unified medical center organization was essential to the future of the institutions because of their interdependence, the rapidly changing environment in which they must operate, and the increasing external pressures to expand their programs. This required speaking with a single voice and the development of effective mechanisms for joint planning and decision making so that the resources of each could be efficiently directed at their common goals. The report warned that there were both disadvantages and dangers in continuing the *status quo*.

Four options for the formation of a unified center were presented as guidelines. The option the consultants recommended was the formation of a medical center authority which would be delegated authority by agreement of each parent board for specific and special affairs that were joint concerns of both hospital and medical school. Any matters necessitating corporate action would be ratified by the hospital and university trustees. Thus, each trustee body would continue its direct authority and legal responsibility for its respective institution. There would be a chief executive officer of the center responsible to the medical center authority, with a staff appropriate for carrying out his responsibilities; all expenses incurred would be financed equally by the medical school and hospital. A shopping list of functions that might be delegated was appended to the report. It was suggested that the medical center authority might be made up of the Board of Visitors with several members from each trustee body.

The joint committee in turn requested that key administrative personnel and faculty review the consultants' report on a confidential basis and give the committee members their reaction and recommendations. From these joint meetings, unanimous opinion developed favoring the creation of a unified medical center authority as recommended by the consultants.

The process followed throughout this study is given in some detail at this point because of subsequent events. The focus was on developing an effective partnership relationship between the two institutions and all of those in key positions were given the opportunity to express their opinions during the study and critique the consultants' report and recommendations.

Unfortunately, the entire matter became highly politicized because of the unauthorized distribution of the consultants' report to the officers of the Baptist State Convention by a hospital administrator. This individual had been lobbying actively among hospital trustees and convention officials for the position of chief executive officer and was indicating to them that the whole study process was designed from the start by the medical school as a means for the university to take control of the Baptist Hospital. The illness of Reid Holmes prevented him from properly assessing this situation. As a result, the Baptist State Convention in November 1971 requested a Committee of Fifteen under the chairmanship of Dr. Cecil Sherman, pastor of the First Baptist Church in Asheville, to study the relationship of the hospital to the convention. This committee held several meetings at the medical center interviewing a number of hospital personnel and several representatives of the medical school. It is noteworthy that the joint committee and Committee of Fifteen at no time met together or officially exchanged information.

Meanwhile, the joint committee continued its deliberations in this tense atmosphere, and submitted its final report to the respective trustees and Board of Visitors in September 1972, again after suggestions and approval by the executive officers of both institutions. This report[4] concluded that the two institutions should be formally organized as a medical center and that, in due time, the center should

127

answer to Wake Forest University through its board with a separate governing body appointed from the Wake Forest trustees to direct the medical center. Each institution would continue to retain its respective fiscal responsibilities. To facilitate this, they recommended that an interim committee be appointed and specifically directed to:

1) work out a plan of governance for the medical center by direct day-to-day contact with the problems involved; and

2) develop a plan to bring the medical center under the Wake Forest University Board of Trustees.

This was not the first time such a plan had been suggested. In 1950 the Baptist State Convention appointed a Committee of Nineteen to survey their institutions and agencies. The committee report, which was approved by the convention in 1951, included the statement, "The close relationship of the Baptist Hospital and the Bowman Gray School of Medicine indicates a possible need for a merger of the boards of trustees of these institutions which could mean that the hospital would be recognized as a part of Wake Forest College."[5] A study of this matter was suggested but there is no record that it was carried out.

The interim committee was to have four representatives from each trustee body and the Board of Visitors, plus a representative from the Executive Committee of the General Board of the Baptist State Convention of North Carolina and a clinical faculty member. Also recommended was an internal Medical Center Advisory Council that would consist of the key administrators of each institution and faculty representatives who would be responsible to the interim committee. The council's primary concern would be long-range planning, program coordination, hospital affiliations, fund raising, public relations and promotion of the medical center concept.

The chairman of the Committee of Fifteen, however, had presented his own opinions on this entire matter to the General Board of the Baptist Convention in August 1972 and these had received broad coverage in the media and Baptist press.

In view of the political environment, the hospital and university trustees in October 1972 approved a resolution establishing a committee of medical center trustees consisting of eight members from each trustee body. This board was to consider matters involving both institutions, define how the board could best carry out its mission, and make recommendations relating to the organization of the medical center.

In the following month the recommendations of the Committee

of Fifteen were presented to the Baptist Convention. In brief, these included 1) a call to define the working relationship between the hospital and medical school to protect the integrity of each, 2) the establishment of a medical center trustee committee (eight from each body) to consider matters involving the center and future operations, with recommendations to be made to their respective boards; 3) the establishment of an intramural staff advisory committee with alternating cochairmen from each institution; and 4) the appointment of members of the Board of Visitors by the medical center committee, to which they would make recommendations. This report was approved by the convention. However at this point, the Rev. Boyce Brooks, then chairman of the hospital trustees, offered a resolution that stated that the recommendations of the Committee of Fifteen just approved "will not be implemented in any way that will infringe upon, or prevent the duly elected trustees of the institution from discharging their duties as imposed upon them by the North Carolina Baptist Convention."[6] The Brooks resolution was approved, effectively negating any of the recommendations of the Committee of Fifteen, which the hospital trustees did not wish to implement. This wise and courageous move protected the integrity of the hospital trustees; however, all of these events had a considerable bearing on the form of the medical center organization and governance that was ultimately adopted. To sharpen the focus of Baptist financial contributions to the hospital, the trustees agreed with the recommendation of the Committee of Fifteen that funds received annually from the convention's Cooperative Program would be designated specifically for the School of Pastoral Care and the Mother's Day offering for the care of the needy.

In October 1973 the medical center trustee committee appointed the year before by the two trustee bodies recommended an organization and governance in the form of a legal agreement. This was approved and signed by both parties in February 1974.[7] Much credit is due the committee chairman, Francis Garvin, in forging an acceptable compromise while retaining principles that would allow the medical center organization to function. The agreement established a Joint Administrative Board of the medical center, consisting of 17 members: eight trustees from each institution and one nonvoting professional staff member. Responsibility was delegated to the board for:

–overall supervision of the medical center
–formulation of general policies and planning for the future needs of the center

–acting as spokesman on medical center matters

–serving as a board of adjustment, if necessary

–coordination and support of fund raising

–reviewing and commenting on institutional budgets, affiliation agreements and major construction projects prior to final action by the trustees of the hospital and university

Under this organization, which was similar to that of the Cornell-New York University Medical Center, the final corporate authority of each trustee body was maintained as well as the responsibility for the operation of the medical school and hospital by the dean and hospital president, respectively. The agreement provided for the position of director of the medical center, who was to be nominated by, and responsible to, the joint administrative board and approved by both trustee bodies. Staff was provided and the operation of the new center was to be financed equally by the two institutions. It was provided also that the director would attend meetings of the respective trustees to report on medical center matters. He would be a nonvoting member of all administrative committees and councils of the hospital and medical school, and would be consulted in the preparation of the annual budgets of each institution. The Board of Visitors of the medical center would serve in an advisory capacity to the Medical Center Board and its director, with new members to be approved by the university and hospital trustees.

The Joint Administrative Board elected Rev. Frank Campbell as its first chairman, developed its own bylaws, appointed Dr. Meads as director of the medical center and approved a staff organization that included offices of development, information and publications and facilities planning. With the same person holding the positions of director of the medical center and vice president for health affairs, the latter position properly became staff in relation to the president of Wake Forest, and the dean of the school of medicine reported directly to the president.

In November 1975, the center was officially incorporated and classified by the Internal Revenue Service as a 501(c)3 entity. This allowed the medical center itself to receive charitable gifts and grants. As such, the joint trustee body became the Medical Center Board of Directors. This action did not require the approval of the Baptist State Convention, as no change in functions was involved and a precedent had been established with the incorporation of the School of Pastoral Care Foundation without prior approval of the convention.

Statewide Program of Medical Education in North Carolina

In the early 1970s the shortage of physicians in North Carolina was emerging as a major political issue. The state ranked 43rd in the country in the number of physicians per 100,000 population. As elsewhere in the nation, this problem was accentuated by greater shortages in rural areas and by a decreasing number of graduates entering the primary care specialties such as family practice.

By the fall of 1971, the three medical schools in the state had expanded their first-year enrollments to 280 (Bowman Gray 76, Duke 104 and the University of North Carolina 100) and were considering further expansion if resources could be made available for additional facilities and faculty. Their projections indicated that this combined number could be increased to 394 by 1980 with more places being made available for qualified North Carolina residents.

Meanwhile at East Carolina University Chancellor Leo Jenkins, who had initiated efforts to establish a new medical school in 1965, was increasing pressures to accomplish this end. He based his case on a serious shortage of doctors in eastern North Carolina and indicated that the new school would accept only state residents, and focus on training family physicians who would soon populate the area. Due to Jenkins' persistence and the strength of representatives from the eastern part of the state in the general assembly, the last chapter in this saga began to unfold.

After the failure of East Carolina University to obtain provisional approval for a two-year medical school, the general assembly in 1971 appropriated funds to establish a one-year program for 20 medical students at that institution. The legislature directed that these students were to transfer to the University of North Carolina School of Medicine for the remainder of their medical education, with the total program thus included under full accreditation status of the four-year school. This action was followed in 1972 by a request from East Carolina University to the newly established Board of Governors of the University of North Carolina system to add a second-year at that institution "to return to the school of medicine at University of North Carolina the right and necessary flexibility required to implement enrollment increases and curriculum changes in its first-year classes which the current cooperative program prevents." The Board of Governors, on the recommendation of a special committee, approved the employment of a panel of nationally recognized consultants. This seven-member panel was chaired by Dr. Ivan L. Bennett, Jr., vice president for health affairs and dean of the School of Medicine, New York University. The major efforts of the consultants were directed at problems related to the number of physicians in North Carolina and their geographic and specialty distribution.

In a separate action in the spring of 1973, the General Assembly set aside $7.5 million in capital funds to begin the construction of an additional medical school facility in the state and established a Medical Manpower Study Commission to study the doctor shortage and report back in January 1974. The commission held public hearings in six small communities in the state and in Raleigh, and called on Dr. Ivan Bennett to give them the findings and recommendations of his panel.

The Bennett panel's 285-page final report was submitted to the Board of Governors in September 1973. It was comprehensive and documented well the physician manpower status in the state at this time and the best national thinking on the issues under consideration.[8]

The consultants stressed that the most significant single determinant of a state's physician manpower was the total number of residency places available within the state, and that the lack of clinical teaching facilities in North Carolina was preventing the expansion of medical school enrollment and residency programs. They urged the Board of Governors "to develop an integrated statewide plan for medical education that will draw on the collective strengths and expertise of the state and private medical schools, will assign responsibility and resources for developing and operating programs, and will utilize, in a coordinated fashion, the many hospitals of the state to develop a network for education, training, and improved medical care." More specifically, their recommendations included collaboration among the three medical schools for the expansion of the UNC Area Health Education Center (AHEC) program throughout the state, the creation of 250–300 new primary care residencies, and the encouragement of further opportunities for North Carolina residents to study medicine at the three schools. As for the last, it was recommended that payments be made to Duke and Bowman Gray on the basis of "parity" with the University of North Carolina School of Medicine, i.e., equal financial support per student and equal tuition charges. Other recommendations included ways and means to increase the number of minority medical students, to expand efforts to recruit physicians to the state, and to establish a monitoring system to evaluate the overall program. They recommended that the resources of the state should not be committed to the establishment of a new four-year school within the university system and that the Board of Governors assign explicitly to the school of medicine at Chapel Hill clear responsibility for all programs of undergraduate, postgraduate and continuing medical education conducted within the UNC system. However, they indicated "if and when additional clinical teaching facilities are established in the state (through the AHEC program), including Greenville, the establishment of an additional school will become a feasible alternative to be weighed against using such new teaching capacity to expand enrollment in existing schools."

The university Board of Governors approved the consultants' report on September 2, 1973 and directed President Friday to prepare recommendations consistent with the report, including an appropriate budget. The administrative officers of Bowman Gray and Duke held extensive discussions with their counterparts at UNC, and with President Friday and his staff. The public-private partnership among the three universities and selected affiliated hospitals to carry out the statewide program was endorsed enthusiastically as a significant contribution to the improvement of health care in North Carolina. The degree of participation was to be decided by each institution. In these discussions, Bowman Gray agreed to plan toward a 16-county Area Health Education Center in northwest North Carolina, develop new residencies in family medicine and in general medicine, pediatrics and obstetrics-gynecology, and expand the entering class to 108 medical students, which would include up to 60% North Carolinians who met the school's admission standards. All of this, of course, was contingent on the ability of the school to obtain the necessary financial resources to expand facilities further and for program support. Planning for facilities expansion was already under way and, with this additional challenge, a new fund-raising effort evolved later which was termed the Medical Center Challenge program.

The Legislative Commission on Medical Manpower met with President Friday in late October 1973 to review the board's recommendations. The concept of "parity" in financial support for increasing the number of North Carolina students in the private schools was met with hostility particularly from a physician member who was a strong proponent of the new school at East Carolina University. In a meeting with President Friday the following day an alternative was worked out. Contingent on obtaining required financing, contractual assurances and facilities, Bowman Gray agreed to expand its entering class in 1975–1976 to 98, with 54 North Carolina students, and in 1976–1977 to 108 with 65 North Carolinians. In return the Board of Governors would increase the capitation grant for *all* North Carolinians enrolled to $7,000 and the tuition remission grant to $1,000. In addition, it was agreed that the state incentive loan program would be expanded to cover all North Carolina students and that Bowman Gray and Duke would participate on an equal basis with UNC in the Board of Governors Scholarship program for financially disadvantaged students. The contract was to include provisions for increases in capitation to correspond with inflation in educational costs in the university system. In addition, assurances were given that the state would not impose special conditions on the school other than those related to fiscal accountability and state residency requirements. It was agreed further that one year's notice would be given by either party if the contract was to be discontinued, with assurances by both parties that obligations to North Carolina students enrolled at that time would be continued. Full financial support was to be made available to Bowman Gray to establish 75 primary care residencies, necessary clinical teaching affiliations and the 16-county Northwest North Carolina Area Health Education Center Program. These agreements were approved promptly by the Board of Governors. President Friday fully recognized that Bowman Gray would have to mount a capital campaign to expand facilities further to accomplish these commitments and graciously agreed to give his personal support where needed.

The administrators of Duke Medical School did not wish to increase the percentage of North Carolina students and, as such, their capitation support was not increased. However, Duke agreed to participate in the proposed primary care residency and AHEC programs. UNC-CH was preparing to expand its entering class from 110 to 160, and the necessary state support was approved. This expansion was achieved in 1976.

The Manpower Study Commission submitted its report to the General Assembly in January 1974.[9] It recommended that the legislature approve and fund the expansion of the AHEC program, but took issue with the recommendation regarding ECU Medical School. Their survey of hospitals inferred that North Carolinians were suffering an economic loss of $6,461,378 each year because citizens were using high cost emergency rooms due to the shortage of physicians. "Thus North Carolinians are paying for an additional medical school every year and not getting it. The only solution is to train more doctors oriented toward general practice." They objected to additional planning studies and recommended the appropriation of $10,200,000 to East Carolina University for a basic medical science facility, operational funds to expand the medical school to a second year and enlargement of the entering class from 20 to 40, continuing to use Chapel Hill's accreditation coverage until separate status was approved. Priority was to be given to an AHEC development in Greenville.

This controversy over the ECU Medical School had been protracted, highly politicized and, at times, bitter. At the request of the medical society in May 1971 the North Carolina Joint Conference Committee on Medical Care undertook a study of the number of additional medical students needed within the state and the most economical and efficient way to educate these students. The conference committee issued a "white paper" in 1973, supporting expansion of the student bodies of the three existing schools as the least expensive and quickest way to alleviate the physician shortage.[10] It recommended phasing out the one-year program at ECU and concluded that the development of a strong AHEC in Greenville, including primary care residencies, was the most effective way to encourage new graduates to practice in eastern North Carolina. This approach was endorsed by the North Carolina Medical Society in May 1973. In February 1974 proponents of the new medical school enlisted the support of the Christian Action League. Its leaders claimed that "the medical establishment in the state had produced the doctor shortage and the ECU people are willing to listen and provide the solution." An editorial in the Chapel Hill newspaper commented that, in seeking the League's assistance, ECU was not looking for their prayers, but their political clout, which had been well demonstrated during the defeat of a state referendum on liquor by the drink in November 1973.[11]

The proponents of the new medical school, however, had the votes, and in April 1974 the General Assembly approved $14 million for a basic science facility at ECU, including a library and animal quarters, and $1 million to cover operating expenses to expand the medical education program. They also approved funds requested by the Board of Governors for the statewide expansion of the AHEC program, including planning grants for Bowman Gray and Duke. A total of $24,999,000 was authorized for the 1974–1976 biennium for teaching, library and other educational facilities in affiliated hospitals and $4,680,000 to supplement a federal grant to the University of North Carolina AHEC for operations. These funds were for the initiation of 75 new primary care residencies and included support for resident stipends, additional faculty, student rotations to community hospitals, library holdings, audiovisual aids, etc. This was a remarkable commitment by the state to the objective of improving access to health care in rural North Carolina. In addition to physicians, AHECs were to provide training and continuing education for nurses, dentists, pharmacists, public health and a variety of technical personnel. The objective was to encourage students to consider practice in smaller communities and help recruit and retain physicians and other health manpower in these areas by reducing professional isolation and enhancing their effectiveness through consultation and education at local community hospitals.

In November 1974, recognizing the reality of the situation, the Board of Governors authorized ECU to proceed with the development of a four-year medical school in association with a new Pitt Memorial Hospital that was financed by state funds. In 1975 the General Assembly approved $43 million for that purpose. The new school was accredited provisionally in April 1977 and fully approved four years later.

With the implementation of the agreements with the Board of Governors, all direct contact between the private schools and state government on this matter ended. Financial support for these institutions was an integral part of the budget submitted by the University of North Carolina Board of Governors each biennium and excellent relations continued with President Friday and his staff. Because of severe constraints in state revenues in the immediate years ahead and the new income from other sources received by the private schools, it was considered prudent not to request inflationary increases in capitation. The increase of 36 places in the entering class committed to North Carolinians at Bowman Gray under the program of state aid was indeed a bargain for the State of North Carolina, when compared with the cost of the new places created through state financing of both the capital and operating costs of a new medical school.

When the ECU School of Medicine received provisional accreditation in 1977, its administration was invited to join the other three schools in quarterly discussions of topics of mutual concern. All institutions

136

have worked cooperatively within the framework of the statewide AHEC program. Much credit for the rapid and orderly development of the academic medical center in Greenville is due Dr. William E. Laupus, who has served as dean since the fall of 1975. Through his leadership the institution has contributed much to the improvement of health care in eastern North Carolina, and the bitter debate is now only history.

The Medical Center Challenge Program

Even as the last phases of construction and renovation under the Medical Center Development program were nearing completion, pressures were beginning to mount for additional academic space and for expanding clinical programs. These needs were becoming apparent due to the rapid expansion in faculty, and particularly as a result of the sectionalization of medicine and pediatrics and the developing challenges of the statewide program in medical education. The latter called for a 40 percent expansion in the medical student body, the formation of a new department of family medicine with an appropriate teaching clinic, and space for the additional faculty and supporting services required to meet these needs. Also, certain elements of the original Medical Center Development program that had been deleted were now looming as essential along with increasing demands for new regional services provided by the medical center, such as renal dialysis, sonics, and perinatal intensive care.

A centerwide study of projected needs was begun in 1972, which culminated in a three-day conference of the center's professional and administrative staff at Pipestem, West Virginia in June 1973. The format was entitled "The Responsibilities of an Academic Medical Center in a Changing Society." As in previous retreats an extensive data base on the center and reports of various task forces dealing with key issues were included in a workbook for all participants. Recommendations evolved which formed the basis for redefining the goals of the center in terms of changes and in the needs of the health care system and a delineation of resources and program priorities required to meet the goals. Primary care emerged as a major issue, and a strong consensus developed within the faculty that the center should become more involved in preparing physicians in this specialty. This consensus paved the way for a decision shortly thereafter to establish a Department of Family Medicine and residency programs

137

in this field with funds that became available through the AHEC program and later from the Bureau of Health Manpower.

In April 1974 planning consultants were employed to develop architectural solutions to meet priority needs for facilities. They were asked to maximize the use of existing property owned by the medical center. In January 1975 the trustees established a committee that included representatives of the Board of Visitors, to study the feasibility of the projected expansion program. A "Medical Center Challenge Fund" was established also to finance further planning and to receive gifts and grants for other program costs. In June the committee confirmed the need for the proposed facilities and the estimated cost of $17,900,000. An outside study had indicated that $10 million could be raised from extramural sources. The remainder would be financed through a pledge by the clinical faculty of $4.5 million; $800,000 from the Area Health Education Center program toward a model family practice clinic, and the rest from hospital and medical school reserves. The trustees gave approval to proceed and, again, the Board of Visitors pledged their full support toward raising the necessary extramural funds.

Plans called for a five-story, 96,000-gross-square-foot Focus Building on the site of the original hospital building (Old Main), a 112,000-square-foot, four-story Family Practice Building next to Queen Street, additional parking facilities, an expanded chilled water system, two horizontal "transportation spines" connecting the Reynolds Tower and Focus Building to the Family Practice Building, and limited renovations. Early on it was agreed by the vice president, dean and the hospital chief executive officer that any addition to this basic program or major change order would have to be financed from internally generated funds. Past history was not to be repeated. This led to some creative financing when the size of the Focus Building was subsequently increased in size by about 80 percent, and remodeling and renovations were more extensive than originally planned.

John Watlington again served as campaign chairman. A strong case for financial support was developed based on the ability of the center to assist in meeting health manpower and regional service needs. The pledge of $4.5 million from the clinical faculty assured prospective donors of the seriousness of the faculty's commitment to these goals. The community phase of the campaign was supported further by a study of the economic impact of the medical center on Forsyth County for the year 1973–1974. This study estimated that of the $48.4 million in medical center expenditures, $34 million flowed into the local economy and that the center was directly responsible for 3,240 jobs and was at the time the third largest private employer. Ketchum and Company was employed again as fund-raising counsel, with Mr. Dallas Mackey assigned as campaign director. Mr. J. Patrick Kelly had replaced Howard Hall in June 1974 as director of development for the medical center. A total of $11,717,264 was raised between May and December 1976. Response from local and state foundations, corporations and individuals was again very gratifying. However, in comparison with prior campaigns, an increased percentage of funds came from out of state, which gave indication that the center had broadened considerably its credibility and reputation during the previous decade.

The Family Practice Building was completed in 1978 at a cost of $5,845,186. It housed the new Department of Family Medicine and the model family practice clinic for patients and their families desiring continuing comprehensive care. In 1974 Dr. Julian F. Keith, a Bowman Gray graduate and family physician, was chosen to head this department and, with his associates, soon developed a credible program for medical student and residency training in this specialty as well as excellent patient care services. Until the new building was completed, the family practice clinic was located temporarily in Old Main. The Family Practice Building was designed to house also the Department of Psychiatry and Behavioral Medicine, clinical offices for neurology, neurosurgery and otolaryngology, the Center for Ultrasound, the hospital medical records department, computer center, and facilities for ambulatory renal dialysis.

During construction the Focus Building was expanded to 178,000 square feet; its total cost was $10.7 million, and it was occupied in 1981. This facility was renamed Watlington Hall in honor of John F. Watlington, Jr., then chairman of the Board of Wachovia Corporation and chief executive officer of Wachovia Bank and Trust Company. Watlington had served as chairman of the Board of Visitors since 1969 and headed both the Medical Center Development and Medical Center Challenge program campaigns that had resulted in the $80-million expansion and renovation of the center over a period of two decades. Watlington Hall included academic space for clinical departments; administrative offices of the medical center, hospital and medical school; basic supporting units and a facility for a new Department of Dentistry. The dental facility was financed primarily by R.J. Reynolds Industries and was associated with a new dental service for Reynolds employees. Dr. Charles Jerge, who had designed the dental care plan and its facilities for Reynolds, was appointed chairman of this new department. Jerge, a nationally recognized expert on the delivery of dental services, is a former dean of the School of Dentistry at the University of Connecticut. The faculty of this department soon added an important new dimension to the educational programs and patient care services of the center. Watlington Hall not only allowed for faculty expansion and consolidation of several centerwide support services, but also freed up space in older medical school buildings for research and for the expansion of the library. During the Challenge program, parking facilities for the medical school were expanded through the 1975 purchase and demolition of the Joy Apartments directly across Hawthorne Road from the institution. The following year a four-deck facility was constructed on the parking lot in front of Reynolds Tower to accommodate patient and visitor needs. In return, the parking was increased in city lots to accommodate the projected expansion in hospital employees.

The final cost of the Medical Center Challenge program was $32.6 million. Renovations were far more extensive than originally planned, in large part due to unanticipated problems with mechanical and electrical systems in original medical center buildings and the necessity of meeting more stringent safety code requirements. These problems added $12.6 million to project costs. Funds to meet the additional expenditures were generated internally from two major sources. Third-party agencies had ruled in 1975 that faculty effort devoted to the training of residents at the center could be reimbursed by imputing these costs by methods used in medical schools and teaching hospitals that were owned and operated by a single corporation. The hospital was allowed reimbursement for these costs retroactively from 1969. There was internal disagreement over which institution had a right to these funds and, as a compromise, they were placed in escrow to be used for projects of mutual benefit. When the over-run in renovation costs became evident, a total of $9.9 million was eventually allocated from the escrow fund for this purpose. A second source was the long term clinical faculty pledge which, as in the past, was a net amount that allowed the institutions to borrow internally against the pledge from their reserves. With the decision to expand Watlington Hall both institutions agreed to waive interest repayments through the pledge and allocate these payments instead to the costs of construction. As a result, a total of $7,777,000 was derived from the pledge for the Challenge program. In all candor, it can be said that the time and effort of the full-time clinical faculty resulted in more than $17 million from these two sources for this construction program. As far as is known, it was a contribution unprecedented in the history of medical education in this country.

The final costs for the Medical Center Challenge program and its associated renovation were $32,599,914, with over 80 percent coming from private sources. The two major buildings were dedicated and the fortieth anniversary of the medical center was celebrated in ceremonies held on September 14, 1981. Gordon Gray, the last living member of the committee that awarded the Bowman Gray Fund to Wake Forest, and a member of the Board of Visitors for 18 years, gave the keynote address entitled "Forty Years of Faith." Tracing the history of the center, Gray stated that without faith we would not be here today and that the faith of the founders (the committee) had been thoroughly vindicated by the tremendous progress over the previous four decades.[12]

Consolidation of Perinatal Services at Forsyth Memorial Hospital and Affiliation with Reynolds Health Center

Facilities to be provided through the Medical Center Challenge program were a major requirement for the center's participation in the statewide program for medical education. However, it was important also that supplemental training sites for the 75 new primary care residents and for Area Health Education Center educational activities be developed.

By a fortunate coincidence, part of these requirements were met through the evolution of the 1971 recommendations of the Forsyth Health Planning Council that had been endorsed by all major health care institutions and organizations in the county and by city and county governments. The recommendations called for phasing out Reynolds Memorial as a general hospital and the use of the facility in part as a family health center, and also for the consolidation of all inpatient perinatal services within the county. The last had been strongly supported by consultants representing the American College of Obstetrics and Gynecology as a means of reducing the high rate of infant and maternal mortality in the county and for greatly improving the clinical training of residents in the area of perinatal medicine. It was agreed that logically this consolidation should take place at

Forsyth Memorial Hospital if proper affiliation agreements could be developed. Baptist Hospital was ruled out for several reasons. Approximately 75 percent of the 4,500 deliveries at that time were at Forsyth Memorial and additional costly facilities would be required at Baptist. Furthermore, obstetrics was considered to be largely a community service, rather than a regional referral service, as indicated by Baptist's obstetrical volume, which was barely marginal for house staff training. County government had assigned the responsibility for developing the family health center to the Forsyth Hospital Authority which had formerly operated Reynolds Hospital and, in light of the need for additional primary care training sites, the medical school initiated negotiations for involving students and primary care residents in this new program.

Critically important discussions began with the Hospital Authority and center administrators and professional staffs that were involved in the affiliations. The process was one of education, followed by negotiation. The medical school first established the basic principles of affiliation that would be necessary to assure proper standards for medical education and to meet accreditation requirements for residency training. In the case of consolidation of services, this included also assurances to diminish the risk of removing a major teaching service from Baptist Hospital. Consolidation required an $8-million expansion and renovation program at Forsyth Memorial toward which AHEC agreed to contribute $200,000 for educational space; the remainder came from bonds issued by the county. AHEC funds could also contribute to salary and other program support for residents assigned to Forsyth Memorial and Reynolds Health Center. Together, these contributions were important to those who could not justify increasing the hospital per diem costs at Forsyth Memorial and fees at Reynolds Health Center to pay for educational costs. The affiliation with Reynolds Health Center was relatively simple to accomplish as the professional staff at Forsyth Memorial was pleased to let the medical school faculty relieve them of that responsibility. However, negotiation on the affiliation with Forsyth Hospital, which had as a goal a teaching relationship with all major services, broke down on several occasions. With time running out for the issuance of bonds, Dean Janeway and Dr. Edward Spudis, chief of staff at Forsyth, finally developed an acceptable compromise which made no substantive changes in intent, and safeguarded accreditation standards as they applied to student and resident training on selected services. The consolidation of perinatal services was organized in a manner agreed to by the obstetrics, pediatric and anesthesia staffs of both institutions. Service-to-service agreements followed in medicine and psychiatry. Surgical back-up was supplied by the clinical faculty of the medical school who had courtesy staff appointments at Forsyth. Access to films and specimens was given to the radiology and pathology faculty of the medical center. As with the medical school's affiliation agreement with Baptist Hospital, the Hospital Authority was responsible for patient care costs of the consolidated service at Forsyth and the County for patient care costs at Reynolds Health Center. The medical school was responsible for educational costs and professional and academic standards on the teaching services. The health center opened under the new agreement July 1 1975. Dr. Ted Chandler was appointed its first medical director. The consolidated perinatal program began in 1977.

After several years the Hospital Authority dropped its relationship with Reynolds Health Center and thereafter the county government has negotiated contracts directly with the medical school for professional services. Both programs have met their objectives well, and much credit is due Dr. Frank C. Greiss, chairman of the Department of Obstetrics and Gynecology, for the smooth implementation and productive relationship that has accompanied perinatal consolidation. This has become a model program of great benefit to the community. The 77-bed service includes an intermediate care newborn nursery and a maternal intensive care unit and is staffed 24 hours a day by professionals representing obstetrics, obstetrical anesthesiology, neonatology and perinatal medicine. Infants requiring more intensive respirator care are managed in the 25-bed neonatal intensive care unit at Baptist Hospital. All county patients are assured the best in perinatal care. This was demonstrated by the sharp drop in rates of infant and maternal mortality, particularly in the black community, shortly after the program was fully implemented. This unit also was designated as the referral center for high-risk mothers from the surrounding region so that its contributions have extended far beyond county lines.

Area Health Education Center (AHEC) Program

The development of a regional AHEC was the third requirement for the medical center if it was to meet its commitments under the statewide plan for medical education. The goals of the state AHEC program were to increase the number and productivity of health manpower in North Carolina and to improve distribution of physicians throughout the state with particular emphasis on primary-care. The methods were the creation of 300 new primary-care residency positions, the rotation of students and residents to selected community hospitals in the state as part of their educational experience, and the development of opportunities for continuing education and consultation for all health manpower at the community level. Through these approaches students and residents would experience first hand the opportunities and challenges of practice in smaller communities. Further, by bringing continuing education and consultation to the local level, professional isolation would be reduced, and the environment of practice in the area favorably enhanced.

The roots of the AHEC concept were seen in several prototypes such as the long-standing educational and consultative link between the Bingham Associates of Tufts Medical School and community hospitals in Maine. However, this approach became more fully conceptualized and developed in this country by Dr. Reece Berryhill while he served as the first director of the division of education and research in community medical care at UNC-CH following his retirement from the deanship.[13]

The Carnegie Commission on Higher Education introduced the term AHEC in 1970 in its special report on the nation's health and recommended that 126 new AHECs be established in association with academic medical centers as a means for improving the geographic distribution of health manpower.[14] As a result of this report, the Comprehensive Health Manpower Act of 1971 included financial support for off-campus professional educational programs organized by medical schools within the regions they served. Mr. Glenn Wilson, who replaced Dr. Berryhill, submitted a proposal under this legislation to develop a statewide AHEC, and the University of North Carolina School of Medicine was awarded a five-year grant of $8.5 million for this purpose in 1972. As mentioned, in 1973 the Bennett committee recommended that the program receive additional state funds and involve Bowman Gray and Duke Medical Schools. As a result, in 1974 the General Assembly made a major commitment to the program through generous appropriations for the construction of educational facilities in affiliated hospitals and for operational support for the development of nine AHECs which were to cover the entire state.

Bowman Gray assumed the responsibility for an AHEC that would serve 16 counties in northwest North Carolina; Avery County was added at its request in 1980. Under contract with the University of North Carolina School of Medicine, Dr. Emery C. Miller served part-time as the first director and Dr. James C. Leist (Ed.D., Southeast Missouri State University) was employed as full-time deputy director. A very productive relationship was established with the UNC-G School of Nursing through the leadership of Dean Eloise Lewis to oversee and support AHEC activities in nursing. From its inception it was stressed that AHEC was an education and training program, and *not* a health service delivery, or a cost or quality control, mechanism. This concept was helpful in gaining rapid acceptance and cooperation from practicing physicians and hospital administrators and their trustees.

Organizationally, Bowman Gray supplied centralized administrative and faculty support and decentralized primary educational activities to three of the large community hospitals in the region, i.e., Rowan Memorial (Salisbury), Catawba Memorial (Hickory), and Watauga County (Boone). Forsyth Memorial served as a major partner in the primary-care training program. State funds were allocated for the construction of educational space at these cooperating hospitals principally library, meeting rooms and on-call resident quarters. All of the institutions involved were represented on a steering committee that was responsible for determining overall policy and program priorities, and for evaluating results. Continuing education programs conducted locally were based on a local assessment of needs. As the central staff was enlarged, a learning resource network was established that linked the medical school library to all of the 30 community hospitals in the region. Continuing education was expanded to include dentists, pharmacists, and a broad range of allied health personnel. Consultation was made available as requested in areas of hospital management, nursing administration and the like.

Because of his skills and leadership ability, Jim Leist was appointed director of the Northwest Area Health Education Center program in 1979 and assistant dean for Continuing Education. Emery Miller then served as director of medical education for the program and continues to head the rapidly expanding activities of the medical school's Division of Continuing Education as associate dean.

The statewide AHEC program became the model for the country and continues to receive strong support from the University of North

Carolina Board of Governors and the General Assembly. Program evaluation demonstrates that the overall effort has been a very significant factor in increasing the number of primary care physicians and in helping to attract and maintain physicians and other health manpower in smaller communities throughout the state. The end product has been improved quality and access to health care for many formerly underserved areas of the state. The unusual cooperation that has existed since the mid-1960s between the academic medical centers in North Carolina no doubt has been an important factor in this success. Much credit is due also to the support and sensitive direction given to the statewide program initially by Glenn Wilson, later by Dr. Eugene Mayer, and their associates at Chapel Hill.

Accomplishments of the Statewide Program for Medical Education

In response to the physician shortage, the number of places in entering classes of the medical schools in North Carolina increased from 209 to 421 between 1962 and 1978. During the period 164 additional places were created for North Carolina residents. Bowman Gray itself doubled the size of its entering class and more than half of the new places were assigned to state residents.

In addition, the four medical schools established departments of family medicine and added 300 new residency positions in the primary care specialties. Programs were developed for physician assistants or nurse practitioners, other health manpower training programs were expanded, and continuing education for health professionals was made

Entering Medical Students — North Carolina Schools[15]

	1962	1969	1976	1978
Bowman Gray				
Total (NC residents)	53 (29)	79 (37)	108 (64)	108 (65)
Duke				
Total (NC residents)	81 (17)	86 (19)	119 (31)	117 (32)
UNC				
Total (NC residents)	75 (69)	85 (75)	160 (143)	160 (146)
ECU				
Total (NC residents)	—	—	—	36 (36)
Totals	209 (115)	250 (131)	387 (238)	421 (279)

more available by development of the statewide AHEC system. These accomplishments represented a unique cooperative partnership between many private and public institutions that responded at this time to a critical social need. Equally remarkable was the outpouring of private and public financial support that was essential to make this response possible.

Strengthening the Infrastructure During the 1970s

The successful implementation of the three major components required for the medical center to meet its commitments under the statewide plan for medical education, i.e., facilities expansion, educational affiliations, and AHEC, have been described separately to give some historical clarity to these important events. However, at this point the story must return to the mid-1970s to take proper note of the internal developments that were of equal importance in contributing to institutional development and the success of the programs.

During his initial years as chief executive officer of the hospital, John Lynch gave primary attention to the establishment of a strong administrative team, the development of management information and control system, and preparations for expanded patient services accompanying the opening of the Reynolds Tower. Several key administrative appointments were made during this period which were proven sound through their subsequent contributions and long tenure.

Miss Joyce Warren retired as director of nursing in March 1973, after 21 years of loyal and valuable service to the hospital. She also had served as director of the school of nursing until August 1972. Mrs. Gwen Andrews, the associate director of nursing, was promoted to director when Miss Warren retired and has served with distinction since that time.

Len Preslar joined the staff of the hospital business office in 1971. His overall management and financial skills became quickly apparent, and he advanced rapidly to the position of controller in 1974, and vice president for financial management in August 1975. Two senior administrators who had served the institution well under Reid Holmes continued under Lynch. Mr. Reuben Graham, who came to the hospital in 1950 as assistant administrator and purchasing agent was designated vice president for general services. He retired in January 1981, with 31 years of dedicated and loyal service to the institution. Gerald Hewitt, who had been with the institution since 1965 as manager of the business office was made vice president for patient financial services in January 1973. The Rev. W.K. McGee, who had served as director of the department of denominational relations since 1945, retired in 1971. The Rev. Calvin Knight was appointed his successor in June 1971. This department serves as an important communications link between the hospital and Baptist churches throughout the state.

The hospital established a Department of Social Services in 1973, with Mrs. Betty Neal Bodenhamer as director. The clinical faculty had for many years urged Reid Holmes to set up such a department, but he insisted that selected nurses could deal with county departments of social services in patient discharge planning and that hospital chaplains adequately covered other services such as assistance to families of needy patients. The new department brought needed expertise to increasingly comprehensive patient care as well as providing relief for nurses and chaplains alike.

New patient care facilities came on line rapidly beginning with the Z. Smith Reynolds Foundation Tower, which was occupied in stages during 1972; the last element, a 38-bed intensive care unit, opened in March 1973. The tower was dedicated on the fiftieth anniversary of Baptist Hospital and celebrated in ceremonies held on May 26. The opening of a 25-bed psychiatric nursing unit on the third floor of the Progressive Care Center followed in March 1974; the Ambulatory Care Building in March 1975; and finally the clinic facilities in the Family Practice Building in June 1978. Kembly Inn had been demolished and additional parking became available for hospital employees on this site in June 1973.

A regional ambulatory dialysis progam was initiated in 1975 by the medical school in special facilities provided in the Family Practice Building under the supervision of Dr. Vardaman Buckalew, head of the Section of Nephrology. The first computerized axial tomography (CAT) scanner in North Carolina was installed in the Department of Radiology in July 1975. Extensive renovations of west and south buildings, which were begun in 1973, were finally completed in January 1977, overlapping the next phase of construction initiated under the Medical Center Challenge program. A six-bed burn unit made possible through grants from the Kate Bitting Reynolds Health Care Trust and the Duke Endowment was opened in July 1979 as one of four such regional services in the state. The licensed bed capacity of the hospital at this time was 701. It has been said that the road to progress is continually under construction. This has been a truism at the medical center since the mid-1960s.

A number of significant changes related to administration, finances, faculty and program development were implemented in the medical school by Dean Janeway.

In 1973, Dr. Thomas Irving, chairman of the Department of Anesthesia, replaced Dr. Eben Alexander as chief of Professional Services of North Carolina Baptist Hospital. Alexander had served in this position since 1953 and his contribution to the overall improvement of the quality of patient care in the institution stands unmatched. During this period he served also as head of the Section of Neurosurgery, was a major participant in the medical center policy and planning process, and was active on committees of the National Institutes of Health, national neurosurgical societies and in health affairs on the state and community levels. His integrity and loyalty to the center are lasting hallmarks.

During 1975 Dr. Alvin Brodish, University of Cincinnati School of Medicine, had replaced Dr. Sheldon Skinner as chairman of Physiology and Pharmacology; Dr. John Tolmie became associate dean for Student Affairs; Dr. Joseph Gordon was appointed first director of Minority Affairs; and a new Department of Medical Social Sciences and Marital Health was formed with Dr. Clark Vincent as chairman. Vincent was awarded a grant of $500,000 from the Kellogg Foundation in 1976 to expand the educational programs of the department and involve residents in family medicine. When Vincent retired in 1977 after a distinguished career, these activities were continued under the Section of Marital Health and Psychology in the expanded Department of Psychiatry and Behavioral Medicine. Dr. Nat E. Smith, University of Illinois College of Medicine, was appointed associate dean in charge of medical education in 1976 and soon developed strong central support and evaluation services in this area. Dr. Donald M. Hayes resigned in that year to accept the chairmanship of the Department of Community Medicine at the University of Texas Health Sciences Center (Houston). Community medicine was then reorganized as a section in the Department of Family Medicine.

An innovative and productive outreach program for cancer treatment and research was established in 1976 under the leadership of Dr. Charles Spurr. Known as the Piedmont Oncology Association (POA), it consists of a cooperating group of oncologists who practice in the region. Its purpose is to enhance the transfer of newly developed methods of treatment and prevention of cancer from universities to patients in communities through the rapid exchange of information on these new methods and the sponsorship of clinical trials to evaluate further their efficacy. The medical center serves as a resource for assistance in diagnosis and establishment of protocols for clinical trials. Treatment is carried out by POA members in the patient's home community, and the participating physician collects the scientific information needed for the medical center to evaluate results. The initial program was aided by grants from the Kate B. Reynolds Health Care Trust, Duke Endowment and the Self Foundation. At this writing the POA has 120 members who are practicing throughout North Carolina and adjoining states. More than 7,800 patients have been involved in clinical studies and 70 publications in national scientific journals have resulted from the clinical research. The program demonstrates that community oncologists can collect effectively the critical research data needed to evaluate cancer therapy. The National Cancer Institute adopted the pioneering program in 1982 as a model for expansion nationally. In that year, Spurr's grant application for $1.5 million to expand the POA was approved with the highest priority score.

The academic community was saddened by the sudden death of Dr. Norman Sulkin in November 1975. Sulkin had served as chairman of the Department of Anatomy since 1959, had gained national recognition as a neuroanatomist and had established the first Ph.D. program at the medical school. Dr. Keith O'Steen, Emory University School of Medicine, was appointed to replace him in 1977. Also during 1977, Dr. I. Meschan asked to be relieved of his administrative duties, and Dr. C. Douglas Maynard was elected to the chairmanship of the Department of Radiology. Meschan, who had served in that position for 22 years, was the major architect in the development of a department which was highly respected nationally and maintained on the forefront of radiologic technology. He authored numerous textbooks and is well known for his excellence as a teacher. Dr. Cornelius F. Strittmatter, IV requested that he be allowed to return to full-time academic activities after serving 17 years as chairman of the Department of Biochemistry. Dr. Moseley Waite, a senior and very productive member of the department, was chosen to replace him in July 1978. In the same year, Dr. John H. Felts, Jr., became associate dean for admissions.

Janeway established a sound system of cash management during the mid-1970s, under which departmental research and development funds, the plant fund and daily receipts of the Department of Clinics were pooled and invested in short-term financial instruments. As this pool of funds grew, and as rates of interest increased to historically new highs in subsequent years, earned interest became a significant source of unrestricted income for the school. The medical school budget was fully consolidated by including several elements that had been budgeted separately in prior years such as Amos Cottage and the administrative expenses of the Department of Clinics. The medical service plan was rationalized further in July 1977 through the introduction of an institutional umbrella plan. This plan provided additional restraint on the clinical income of certain specialties by placing a surtax on income above specific levels, which at the same time preserved the medical school's long-standing incentive principle in professional patient care.

A milestone in annual alumni giving was passed in 1975-1976 when the level exceeded $100,000. This was due in part to the growth of membership in the Dean's Division that was established in that year at the suggestion of Dr. Jean Bailey Brooks, then president of the Medical Alumni Association. Membership requires annual gifts to the medical school of $1,000 or more and becomes an important stimulus to the continued growth in this fund which has been used to meet high priority needs of the institution.

Faculty expansion proceeded rapidly during the 1970s, as required by the enlarged medical student body, new residency training and research programs, and increasing demands for patient care. By 1977 there were 308 full-time faculty, and crowding of medical school facilities was becoming a serious problem. This was relieved temporarily by relocating several administrative units and research programs to Twin Castles apartments and to a two-story office building adjoining medical center property which was purchased by the Medical Foundation in July 1976. The prolonged period of renovation of older medical school buildings begun in 1970 was finally completed in January 1978.

During 1977, Baptist Hospital and Bowman Gray School of Medicine again received full accreditation for the maximum allowable times which further attested to the remarkable effort that had been made by the faculty and the entire center staff in responding to the health care needs and economic instability of the times.

As noted earlier the Medical Center Corporation was established "to facilitate and enhance the common objectives and goals" of Baptist Hospital and the Bowman Gray School of Medicine. The four-fold core missions of the center had been part of the discussions at the center-wide retreat in June 1973. This statement of mission was approved later by the governing bodies and is as follows:

The Bowman Gray School of Medicine of Wake Forest University-North Carolina Baptist Hospitals, within the limits of its resources as an academic medical center, commits itself to contribute to society by striving

To provide superior education for students and teachers of medicine and related health professions;

To render a continuum of exemplary and efficient patient care in an environment which emphasizes scholarship and human dignity;

To foster the discovery and application of new knowledge through basic and clinical research in the biomedical and relevant social sciences; and

To cooperate with the community, region, and nation through active participation in efforts to improve the health care delivery system.

In addition to the office of the director, the corporation had a small operational staff which supported center-wide development activities, information and publications and facilities planning and construction. Following the completion of the Medical Center Challenge campaign, Wake Forest initiated Phase III of its Sesquicentennial fund-raising effort. Under the university "treaty of 1967" the medical center again restricted its fund raising in the private sector to noncompeting sources such as alumni, grateful patients, and foundations that made grants only to health and medicine. On the advice of fund-raising counsel, the development office was restructured to emphasize deferred and alumni giving and approaches to selected health and medical foundations. In September 1978 Mr. Dallas Mackey, who had served as director of the Challenge Fund campaign for Ketchum, Inc., was employed by the medical center as director of Development. A special center annual report was initiated in 1974 and distributed widely to foundations, government agencies, previous donors to the institution, alumni and referring physicians. Media contacts were expanded and an intramural monthly publication, *Around the Medical Center,* was begun for all employees.

Although each institution had planning mechanisms, the first coordinated center-wide strategic plan was developed in 1978. This was reviewed critically and approved by the Board of Visitors and Medical Center Board, and subsequently by both trustee bodies. This comprehensive plan, and up-dates in subsequent years, served as a valuable mechanism for both the education and involvement of governing and advisory boards and for developmental purposes. The center's organization served its purpose because its services were mutually supportive. Coordination between the two institutions was achieved through center-wide planning and frequent communication between the three chief executive officers and by their active participation in meetings of governing bodies. The organization was cumbersome, however, in that it involved two boards and two trustee bodies. This required a number of formal meetings with each of those groups annually, which at times contributed to a delay in the decision-making process. Further, the official and lengthy name of the corporation—The Medical Center of the Bowman Gray School of Medicine and the North Carolina Baptist Hospital—was forged through compromise and created obvious problems of identity that have not yet been resolved.

Legacies of the 1970s—Prelude to the 1980s

Economic circumstances and changes in federal health policy that occurred during the 1970s had a major impact on academic medical centers in this country. These factors served as a prelude to new challenges faced by these institutions in the years ahead, and several of the more important ones will be reviewed briefly at this point.

This decade was a period of rapid growth for all academic medical centers. Under the stimulus of federal health manpower initiatives, their number grew from 101 to 126 and physician graduates more than doubled, reaching 15,135 by June 1980. This rise had been paralleled by an even greater growth in full-time faculty, particularly in the clinical specialties. Although federal aid for biomedical research and education continued to increase somewhat even in constant dollars, growth within medical schools was financed increasingly from nonfederal sources such as medical service income, tuition and state appropriations. However, the hard fought financial gains were eroded throughout this decade by continuing inflation and high interest rates—the product of federal deficit spending and an excessive money supply. Over the ten-year period the Consumer Price Index (CPI) doubled and the dollar lost half of its value. The viability of many teaching hospitals became heavily dependent on Medicare and Medicaid. As reimbursement was based retrospectively on costs, this gave some protection to these labor intensive institutions whose wage scales were continually under pressure from local competition and labor unions.

The growth in medical student enrollment was so rapid following the federal incentives of the 1960s that the government's goal of increasing the number of new physicians by 50 percent by 1975 was achieved one year earlier and the development of new medical schools was still in progress. Congress was made aware that a possible surplus of physicians could occur, and so passed legislation in 1976 to restrict the inflow of foreign medical graduates whose entry to this country had been given a high priority during the period of physician shortages. In addition, a Graduate Medical Education National Advisory Committee (GMENAC) was chartered and directed "to make recommendations to the Secretary [Department of Health and Human Services] on present and future supply of, and requirements for, physicians, their specialties and geographic distribution. . . ." This committee submitted an initial report in 1979 and a final report in September 1980.[16] Among the conclusions were an estimated surplus of 70,000 physicians by 1990. Excesses were projected in 15 specialties, a balance between supply and demand in eight and shortages in four. The report recommended that medical schools reduce class size, that no new schools be established, and that the number of foreign medical graduates entering the United States be severely limited. Continuing federal support was advocated for residency programs in family practice and other specialties in short supply and for ambulatory care experience for students. Reaction to the report was varied and debate continues regarding the validity of the assumptions and methodology used by the committee. Nonetheless, the GMENAC report focused attention on a problem that was to become a major concern during the 1980s. This concern was heightened because of the proliferation of proprietary medical schools of poor quality in the Caribbean that catered to United States citizens unable to gain admission to accredited schools in this country.

Academic medical centers not only increased in size during this decade, but also in the diversity of their organization and function. Some were research intensive, some consisted of multiple schools and hospitals which conducted a wide variety of health manpower educational programs, and still others, particularly in major urban centers, assumed large health burdens for the care of the poor.

Favorable public attitudes toward institutions in general, including government, religion, law and medicine, began to wane. Their failure to solve many social problems, the emerging realization that dollars alone do not produce solutions, and Watergate, all contributed to a growing disillusionment and distrust. Academic medical centers were not excluded from criticism. They were asked and were unable to solve national problems beyond the scope of their mission, problems that had important social or economic ramifications, such as drug addiction, child abuse, stress in the workplace, population control and even environmental pollution.

From the standpoint of health policy, the major issue that emerged in the 1970s was the rapid increase in national health care expenditures. Between 1965—the year that Medicare and Medicaid legislation was enacted—and 1980, total expenditures had increased at an average annual rate of 12.5 percent and, as a component of the gross national product, the increase was from 5.9 to 9.8 percent. This cost escalation was a reflection of three decades of stimulus to both the supply and demand side of the health care equation. It was exacerbated during the 1970s by the general inflation of the period and the lack of financial incentives to contain costs through the efficient management of health care resources. On the other hand, unlike basic commodities, health care at the end of the decade was a much different and more comprehensive product than in 1965. Major advances had been made in scientific knowledge and technology and, to their credit, Medicaid and Medicare, by decreasing the financial barriers of the past, had greatly improved access to medical care for the poor and aged.

Federal concern for rising health care costs appeared early in the decade through piecemeal and incremental legislation aimed primarily at hospitals which were the major and most rapidly increasing segment of national health care expenditures. These included mandated utilization review (1972), an attempt to stimulate the development of alternate health care delivery systems (HMOs) (1973), capital expenditure controls through certificate-of-need program (1974), and toward the end of the decade, restriction of Medicare payments to levels that were below actual costs. These approaches were largely ineffective, but they greatly increased administrative work loads in academic medical centers and the complexity of management. On the other hand, as noted before, Medicare and Medicaid were critical in maintaining the viability of many teaching hospitals, as these sources of funds made up from 35 to 50 percent of total revenues and covered many patients who would have been treated previously as "charity care."

The relationship between government and academic health centers also changed in the mid-1970s. Since World War II, both had benefited from a partnership which had resulted in major advances in health care through biomedical research, by increasing the number and quality of physicians and other health manpower, by expanding continuing education, and by initiating programs to improve access to care in rural and inner-city areas. However, this symbiotic relationship turned into an adversarial one when government began to use overtly the leverage of federal aid to medical education to intrude on admission policies. This occurred in 1976 with the passage of PL 94-484, which included the so-called "Guadalajara clause." This law required medical schools, as a condition of continued eligibility for federal capitation grants, to accept a quota of United States citizens who had been enrolled for at least two years in a foreign medical school and who had passed the Part I examination of the National Board of Medical Examiners. Fortunately, this legislation was repealed after one year. However, general capitation support was then decreased and eligibility for an increasing number of federal aid programs began to deal selectively with specific modifications in curriculum, residency training programs, and the like. Increasingly one heard from government officials that academic medical centers were the cause of problems and not the solution. This unfortunate turn of events only served to stress these institutions further, as was well described by Rogers and Blendon.[17]

One additional trend became evident toward the end of the decade that was to have an important influence on the years ahead. Debate was intensifying at this time on the merits of regulating versus stimulating competition (the free-market system) as the best approach for containing health care costs. Arnold Relman, editor of the *New England Journal of Medicine*, published an article entitled "The New Medical-Industrial Complex" that received immediate national attention.[18] He pointed out the relatively unheralded rise of a huge new industry that supplied health care services for a profit. It included proprietary hospital chains, nursing homes, diagnostic laboratories, home care, free standing emergency clinics and a wide variety of other services which had a total gross income in 1979 of about $35 to $40 billion. The pharmaceutical and hospital supply industries were not included in these figures. He further said that, although this complex may be more efficient than their non-profit counterparts, it creates problems of overuse and fragmentation of services, overemphasis on technology, "cream-skimming" and the possibility of exerting undue influence on national health policy. The article further intensified debate but left no doubt that competition was an established fact in health care delivery and a major force to be reckoned with in the immediate future. Also about this time medicine was increasingly referred to as a business, hospitals as an industry and patients as consumers. This change was to be followed by publications on "marketing" hospitals and medical practice and the use of other terms formerly common only in business and industry. Although it had become essential to introduce some of the techniques and skills of modern corporate management into the operation of hospitals and schools of medicine, to many professionals these terms gave a negative image of medicine and depersonalized the important doctor-patient relationship.

References and Notes

1. Annual Report of the Baptist State Convention of North Carolina 1971, pp. 197–198; 523.
2. The consultants were: Mr. John M. Danielson, director of the Council on Teaching Hospitals and Health Services, Association of American Medical Colleges; Dr. Marjorie P. Wilson, director of the Department of Institutional Development AAMC; and Dr. William N. Hubbard, Jr., vice president, Upjohn and Company and former dean, University of Michigan School of Medicine.
3. A study for the ad hoc Joint Committee of the Trustees of the Bowman Gray School of Medicine of Wake Forest University and the North Carolina Baptist Hospital, Winston-Salem, North Carolina, October 1, 1971.
4. Report of the ad hoc Committee appointed by the Board of Trustees of the North Carolina Baptist Hospital, the Board of Trustees of Wake Forest University and the Board of Visitors of the Bowman Gray School of Medicine to study the Future Development of

the Medical Center, September 7, 1972 (marked "Confidential").

5. Annual of the Baptist State Convention of North Carolina, 1951, p. 46.

6. Annual of the Baptist State Convention of North Carolina, 1972, p. 93.

7. Agreement Establishing a Medical Center Joint Administrative Board, February 28, 1974.

8. A Statewide Program for Medical Education in North Carolina: Report of a Panel of Medical Consultants to the Board of Governors of the University of North Carolina September 1973.

9. Report of Medical Manpower Study Commission to the 1974 General Assembly.

10. Subcommittee on Medical Students and Medical Manpower, North Carolina Joint Conference Committee on Medical Care, North Carolina Medical Journal 34: 210-215 (March) 1973.

11. Editorial, The Chapel Hill Newspaper, February 18, 1974.

12. "The Medical Center: Forty Years of Faith," address by Mr. Gordon Gray September 14, 1981 on the occasion of the dedication of the Medical Center's Watlington Hall and Family Practice Building.

13. Berryhill, W. Reece, Blythe, Wm. B. and Manning, Isaac H.: Medical Education at Chapel Hill: The First Hundred Years, pp. 162-167, UNC at Chapel Hill 1979.

14. Carnegie Commission on Higher Education: Higher Education and the Nation's Health; Policies for Medical and Dental Education, pp. 55-59, October 1970.

15. Source, JAMA, Education Numbers: November 16, 1963; November 23, 1970; December 26, 1977; March 7, 1980. Note: Figures do not exclude the occasional student who repeats the first year.

16. Graduate Medical Education National Advisory Committee, "Report to the Secretary, Department of Health and Human Services" September 1980.

17. Rogers, D.E. and Blendon, R.J. "The Academic Medical Center: A Stressed American Institution," N E J Med. 298: 940-950, (April 27) 1978.

18. Relman, A.S., "The New Medical-Industrial Complex," N E J Med. 303 (17): 963-970 (October 23) 1980.

CHAPTER VIII

Entering the Decade of the Eighties

Academic Medical Centers Face Changing National Health Policies

As noted, national health care expenditures had escalated sharply since 1965 reaching $278 billion in 1980. They were projected to increase to $798 billion by 1990 if no reforms occurred. A strong consensus had developed among government, business, labor, the insurance industry and those providing patient care that more stringent cost containment measures were essential. Emphasis was given to developing a more cost-effective health care delivery system and to decreasing its utilization. National debate centered on whether this could be accomplished best through increased regulation or by stimulating competition. The conservative mood of the country was reflected in the election of Ronald Reagan as President in 1980, tipping the balance toward competition. Retrenchment occurred in many social programs spawned during the Johnson administration, and responsibility for their administration was shifted to the states with federal financing in the form of block grants. The general excess in physicians and hospital beds that was becoming apparent in this country enhanced the probability that measures to encourage the "free-market" approach would be effective.

Projections of the new environment in which academic medical centers would operate during the 1980s were summarized briefly in the medical center Annual Report for 1980–1981:[1]

All indications point to the 1980s as the *Decade of Competition* for academic medical centers. Demographic and economic trends will result in greater competition for well qualified students and young faculty. The growing disparity between available research dollars and the cost of conducting research will further increase competition for extramural support. The projected surplus of physicians already apparent in larger urban areas, and the emergence of alternate health care delivery systems, including for-profit networks, will sharpen competition for patients. If proposed federal legislation aimed at stimulating price competition is enacted, teaching hospitals will be particularly disadvantaged unless reimbursement is properly adjusted for their added cost of education, indigent care, and essential, but expensive, tertiary services.

As competition impacts increasingly on each function of an academic medical center, its future will depend largely on its ability to attract and maintain high quality faculty and management talent, generate capital and adapt innovatively to change. This nation has grown and prospered through competition when it is accompanied only by minimum and appropriate regulation. Whether the latter will or should occur in the health care system is now the center of debate. Further, it is also unclear whether our society and the Congress recognize that the financing and quality of medical education, research and patient care programs within each center are closely interwoven and interdependent.

Categorical vision prevails within many of our public and private agencies, and mechanisms at the national level do not exist to evaluate the overall effect of the projected reduction in federal funds for the multiple programs that support the basic mission of the center. The aggregate loss of funding can result in distortions in financing and have a significant negative impact on the quality of a center's programs and its ultimate contributions to our society . . .

The Medical Center at its Fortieth Year

The medical center celebrated its fortieth anniversary on September 14, 1981. The previous 15 years had been a time of major growth in resources, programs and services which had placed the center in a sound position to face the rapid changes that were occurring in the delivery and financing of health care and in medical education. Comparative statistical indicators shown in Table I reflect this during this period. The year 1965 was chosen as the baseline as it was just prior to the beginning of a major facilities expansion accomplished through the Medical Center Development and Challenge programs, and just before a major infusion of government funds for patient care through Medicare and Medicaid. These events and rapid advances

TABLE I
MEDICAL CENTER GROWTH—COMPARATIVE STATISTICS[2]

	1965–1966	1980–1981
Center plant size (gross square feet)(a)	690,910	1,406,200
Center employees	1,694	4,920
(Full-time faculty)	(139)	(377)
Patient Care		
Hospital beds (average in use)	469	657
Patient discharges	18,712	22,834
Total patient days	146,498	205,546
Obstetrics admissions	10,265	0
Occupancy rate (average)	85.6%	85.7%
Ambulatory patient visits	141,880	235,341(b)
(Department of Clinics)	(69,985)	(169,960)
(Outpatient Department)	(56,435)	(32,802)
(Emergency Department)	(15,460)	(32,579)
Employees per patient day	2.8	4.37
Educational Programs		
Medical students	210	431
House officers and fellows	102	388
Graduate students	47	94
Allied Health students	102	246(c)
Nursing education	202	361(c,d)
Pastoral Care	21	53
Continuing Education participants	328	11,821
Research and Demonstration programs		
Extramural grants/contracts, expenditures	$ 3,237,600	$ 15,291,200
Faculty publications	209	472
Center library expenditures	$ 62,460	$ 782,300
Institutional Finances		
N.C. Baptist Hospital		
Total operating expenditures	$ 7,183,090	$ 58,230,000
(In- and outpatient)		
Inpatient cost per patient day	$ 43.30	$ 304
Fund balance	$ 2,623,100	$ 77,063,000
Bowman Gray School of Medicine		
Total operating expenditures	$ 6,738,000(e)	$ 53,519,000
Permanent endowment (market value)(f)	$ 7,537,000	$ 17,623,400
University, general support	$ 50,000	$ 50,000
Tuition, medical student	$ 1,350	$ 4,900

(a) Excludes the 185-acre animal research farm and associated facilities
(b) Excludes visits to Reynolds Health Center
(c) Includes cooperative programs with Forsyth Technical Institute
(d) Includes baccalaureate degree nursing students from UNC-G and Winston-Salem State University
(e) Separately budgeted elements added to achieve proper comparison
(f) Includes trusts held by the Winston-Salem Foundation, whose income is designated for the medical school

in medical science, had a very significant impact on the resources and programs of the hospital and medical school and their status in 1980. Comparisons of financial data must be assessed in terms of the long period of serious inflation and devaluation of the dollar that occurred during this time, but the increasing fiscal strength and expansion of the resources of the two institutions is clearly evident.

The statistical data do not reflect the increasing sophistication of medical care rendered and new diagnostic and therapeutic modalities introduced during this period. These included renal dialysis, open heart surgery, joint replacements, special units for severe burns and for perinatal intensive care, advanced treatment for cancer and new imaging techniques such as sonography, CAT scanning and magnetic resonance imaging. The data also do not indicate the increasing number of patients referred with complex problems from an ever-widening geographic area. However, information on the top ten discharge diagnoses from Baptist Hospital during the 1970s reflects to some extent the shift to more severe and complex illnesses in the inpatient population:

Top Ten Discharge Diagnoses — North Carolina Baptist Hospital

1969–1970*	1980-1981
1. Bronchitis	1. Chronic ischemic heart disease
2. Hypertension, benign	2. Cancer of the lung or bronchus
3. Cataract	3. Coronary atherosclerosis
4. Benign prostatic hyperplasia	4. Chronic renal failure
5. Depressive neurosis	5. Renal calculi
6. Renal calculi	6. Angina pectoris
7. Atherosclerosis, general	7. Cataract
8. Disease of urinary tract	8. Chest pain, type unspecified
9. Malignancy, trachiobronichial	9. Congestive heart failure
10. Inguinal hernia with obstruction	10. Cancer of the cervix

* Excludes obstetrics services, which were discontinued in 1977.

In 1980 Bowman Gray and Baptist Hospital had become well established as a major tertiary care center serving patients primarily from western North Carolina and bordering states. In certain specialties patients came from far beyond this area. The marked increase in the cost per patient day since 1965, though influenced to a large extent by national inflation during this period, reflects also the introduction of many new diagnostic and treatment procedures, the increase in the complexity and intensity of care required by the change in the patient population and the associated requirement for more personnel per patient day. However, on the basis of cost per patient day or per patient stay, these key financial indicators were significantly less than other tertiary centers in the region. This was not only a hallmark of management efficiency, but also placed the hospital in a stronger fiscal position to compete in the cost-containment environment of the 1980s.

The changes in the patient population noted above, as in many other academic medical centers, had made most major teaching hospitals an incomplete environment in which to conduct medical education. As such, opportunities for medical students and primary care residents to participate in the care of patients in affiliated community hospitals and clinics became essential. The medical school was fortunate that such affiliations had been cultivated and that many members of the part-time faculty throughout the region were willing to contribute their time and effort as preceptors on a voluntary basis to this important phase of medical education.

The fifteen-year comparative data indicate also a remarkable growth in students, full-time faculty, research expenditures and scientific publications. Areas of particular research strength that emerged include oncology, atherosclerosis, cerebro- and cardiovascular disease, infectious disease, immunology and cell biology. By 1980 the position of the medical school in obtaining competitive extramural research support had been greatly improved.

In 1981, through a generous gift from the Brenner family of Winston-Salem, the Center for Adolescent Medicine was established in the Department of Pediatrics. One of only 26 in the nation, its purpose was to provide patient care and the training of students and physicians in the special problems involving teenagers.

Despite the recent expansion of medical center facilities, it was evident that under these growth trends additional space would be needed in the near future for patient care programs and research. The size of the medical student bodies had plateaued and, given the predictions of an emerging surplus of physicians, no further increase was warranted. In 1982 the center-wide planning process was focused on defining the projected needs and on the feasibility of financing another major expansion program during this decade.

Reassessment of Medical Center Organization and Governance

In November 1981 the Medical Center Board of Directors, with the endorsement of trustee chairmen, authorized the establishment of a joint committee "to review the existing organization and governance of the medical center and to determine whether it is appropriate to meet the challenges of this decade." This committee was composed of Francis Garvin (chairman), Thomas D. Long and E.J. Prevatte representing the hospital trustees; Weston P. Hatfield and Colin Stokes from the university trustees; and Lyons Gray from the medical center Board of Visitors. The committee received extensive background materials and held separate interviews with the three chief executive officers, clinical department chairmen, the chief and former chiefs of professional services and President Scales.

The center director and dean pointed out that, though significant progress had been made since the establishment of the medical center organization eight years ago, there were inherent complexities that should be corrected. These complexities included two separate trustee bodies with fiduciary authority, a Medical Center Board delegated specific responsibilities by these trustees but without concomitant authority, and a Board of Visitors which was advisory but whose record of contributions to the center was unparalleled. This cumbersome structure had led to some confusion about the roles of these bodies and, on occasion, had led to unfortunate delays in decision making. As such, there was a need for a strong central governing structure capable of making a strategic and unified response to the competitive challenge ahead. Dr. Meads recommended that the entire center be organized under the university trustees as envisioned by the joint committee in 1972; however, if this was not considered feasible, that the existing center organization and governance be significantly strengthened. It was also recommended strongly that the name of the center be changed to Wake Forest University Medical Center. This identification was thought to be important in eliminating confusion in the minds of prospective students, residents and faculty, and government agencies and foundations, and in leaving no doubt that the institution is indeed an *academic* medical center. Concern emerged among a segment of the hospital trustees regarding the options under discussion. They reasoned that any change might threaten the autonomy of that institution, decrease the role of its chief executive officer and harm the relationship between the hospital

Richard Janeway,M.D., Manson Meads,M.D., John E. Lynch,Dr. P.A.

The Medical Center following the Challenge Program 1983.

Wake Forest University, Reynolda Campus 1983

The Medical Center with Winston-Salem center city in background
(1983)

and the Baptist State Convention. Unfortunately, a debate over the new covenant relationship between Wake Forest University and the convention had activated an anti-university element within the Baptist constituency which no doubt influenced some of this thinking.

The final report of the joint committee was submitted in August 1982. Briefly, the recommendations were as follows:

1. That the trustees adopt officially the four-fold mission statement of the medical center

2. That the name of the corporation be changed to Wake Forest University Medical Center while retaining unchanged the name of each institution comprising the center

3. That the present functions delegated to the center by the trustees be retained and that, when the present director retires in July 1983 the position be left open and the director's functions be carried out by the dean and hospital president as co-equals

4. That the chairman of the Board of Visitors be invited to attend meetings of the Medical Center Board

5. That it should be the responsibility of the chairman of the Medical Center Board to see that this plan of organization and governance be assessed for the board annually and reviewed in depth for the board no later than January 1, 1986.

The decision to have the dean and hospital president serve the functions of the director of the medical center as co-equals was an admitted compromise under existing circumstances and posed major challenges. It eliminated an internal mechanism for arbitration and a focal point for the medical center concept. It also placed the staff of the medical center corporation in the difficult position of reporting to "two masters," each of whom shares equally in financing their support.

However, the change in the name of the corporation as recommended was not agreed to by the hospital trustees despite a petition from the faculty of the medical school and the professional staff of the North Carolina Baptist Hospital. The report without the recommendation for the name change was approved subsequently by both trustee bodies.

165

Dr. Meads retired on July 1, 1983, becoming vice president emeritus for health affairs, and Dr. Janeway became vice president for health affairs in addition to his position as dean. The writer will leave it to future historians to assess the effectiveness of the medical center organization and governance that was in place on that date.

References and Notes

1. Report of the Director, Medical Center Annual Report 1980-1981, pp. 4-5.
2. Information sources for Table I: Duke Endowment Reports, Baptist Annuals, Liaison Committee on Medical Education, Medical Center Annual Reports, Medical School Annual Reports and file data.

The medical center may indeed be "the Miracle on Hawthorne Hill" but those who have been a part of its 40-year history know that many remarkable people and a unique community contributed much to making it so.

The early history of the two institutions that form the center established tap roots that have served it well. The two-year medical school had a heritage of high standards. A lofty goal was declared on the establishment of the four-year institution—to develop a small school "second to none." Baptist Hospital was formulated on compassion for the needy and the recognition of the importance of Judeo-Christian precepts in the healing process of both patients and their families.

The early years of the center were a fight for survival. The limited resources from which the center emerged required the utmost in faith and determination but established by necessity a mold of prudence in fiscal affairs. The credibility of a new academic medical center takes time to develop. This is true particularly of a private institution with meager endowments. In the case of Bowman Gray and Baptist Hospital, credibility grew sequentially. Initially, it was evident in the upgrading of the quality of medical care within the community and region, then through the quality and performance of its graduates, and finally through contributions to research and the national reputation earned by many members of its faculty. The medical center has now reached maturity and national recognition. It is being strengthened further by the growing national prestige of Wake Forest University.

Looking back, what made this unlikely venture a success? Gordon Gray asked this question of the center director prior to the fortieth anniversary celebration, and some thoughts given him for that occasion are noted below.

One might separate the answer to the question into two inter-related parts—factors within the center and those characterizing the community in which it developed. Foremost among the internal factors was a unique faculty. This began with a determined dean, those who came with him from Wake Forest, and physicians who left the security of private practice in Winston-Salem to gamble on the future of the fledgling institution. These individuals were followed by promising young men and women, many of whom later developed national reputations but chose to remain at the center despite attractive offers to go elsewhere. "Moose" Morehead termed them "our kind of folks." They were individuals who in times of crisis placed the institution first, ahead of departmental and personal interests. The remarkable financial contributions of the clinical faculty over a period of forty years to capital and program needs of the center stand as tangible evidence of this loyalty and a broad based commitment to the development of a center of excellence.

Another element has been the stability of administration. Over a forty-year period there have been only three medical school deans, each in turn continuing as vice president for health affairs. National experience demonstrates that the half-life of a dean is less than four years. The hospital has experienced only four changes in chief administrative officers during this time, with the last two spanning a period of more than three decades. The difficult early years taught fiscal discipline which has been the hallmark of administration. Modern management techniques and center-wide planning methods were introduced with relative ease as the critical interdependence and increasing complexity of the enterprise evolved. These approaches would have been made with far more difficulty under an unstable administrative relationship. This is not said to discount tensions at the interface of the hospital and medical school; however, these have led for the most part to constructive outcomes.

A third internal factor was the long-standing policy that programs would be initiated and maintained if they met social needs *provided* they could be carried out within the constraints of institutional resources. The facilities expansion in the 1960s was a response to the national call to train more physicians, as well as for the expansion of biomedical research capabilities and the regionalization of specialized and costly medical technology. In the 1970s the center responded to the need to increase opportunities for North Carolinians to study medicine. This was followed by programs to help correct the shortage of primary care physicians and the poor distribution of health manpower within the state. Also during that time, the center took an active role in helping to meet major problems in health care within the community. As resources have permitted, high-technology diagnostic and treatment services have been established to support the needs of physicians and community hospitals throughout the region. Planning now looks to the growing needs of our aging population.

Turning to the external elements that contributed much to the development of the center, one must quickly recognize the community of Winston-Salem, its quality of life and its long history of generous philanthropy and corporate citizenship. Particularly important over the last four decades have been the generous financial contributions by the Gray, Reynolds and Hanes families, and the foundations and corporations established and expanded through their leadership. One must add the cooperative relationship between the academic medical centers within the state in program development, a relationship which is perhaps unique in the nation. Though relations with the Baptist State Convention have been stormy at times, in the long run cool heads have prevailed; and this important constituency contributed much to the early development of the hospital, the care of the needy, and the special aspects of the environment in which patient care is carried out.

In looking back, however, none of these accomplishments would have been possible without the dedicated support and guidance of the Board of Visitors during the past two decades under the successive leadership of Albert Butler and John Watlington. Through the efforts of this board, the alumni and many volunteers throughout the state, an $80-million facilities expansion program was accomplished over a 15-year period. This expansion was the critical element needed to increase faculty, enhance educational programs, accelerate research contributions, extend patient services and assist in financing the total enterprise.

This history reflects a remarkable cooperative effort between an academic medical center and its community which has been of immense benefit to each and to society as a whole. It is a foundation that augurs well for the future.

THE MEDICAL FOUNDATION OF THE BOWMAN GRAY SCHOOL OF MEDICINE OF WAKE FOREST COLLEGE AND THE NORTH CAROLINA BAPTIST HOSPITALS, INC.

With the founding of the Medical Center, a firm policy was established that patients judged unable to pay professional fees would be classified as "service" and cared for by the house staff under the supervision of the attending staff. As private health insurance grew, some of these patients had coverage for all or part of their hospital charges and, in some instance, reimbursement was available for part of their professional care. In 1952 Drs. Frank R. Lock and Howard H. Bradshaw conceived the idea that, if a foundation were established, these then uncollected professional fees might be channeled through it for the use and benefit of the medical center. The respective trustees approved the idea and in April 1952 "The Medical Foundation of The Bowman Gray School of Medicine of Wake Forest College and the North Carolina Baptist Hospitals, Inc." was incorporated as a non-profit charitable and educational entity.

The purpose of the Medical Foundation was broadly defined to promote education, research and service in preventive and curative medicine; to improve facilities of the medical school and hospital, and to aid the two institutions in the education of physicians and other health manpower. It was empowered to receive gifts and bequests, professional fees from the care of service patients, and other professional contributions. The trustees of the foundation were to number between 15 and 35. They were to include at all times the principal administrative officer of the medical school and hospital and the head and one other person from each department of the school and hospital contributing to and participating in the work of the foundation. Twenty-five percent of funds received from professional fees of hospitalized service patients were allocated to a general fund,

171

and the remainder was placed in accounts of the respective departments producing the fund. At the end of the first year the assets of the foundation totaled $103,145 and were derived entirely from professional fees from private health insurance. A program to expand the corpus through outside gifts was not carried out at that time because it would have interfered with the fund-raising campaign for the south wing of the hospital. As mentioned before, when Medicare and Medicaid programs were initiated in 1965, professional fees collected from service patients with this type of coverage were assigned to a special account. From this, 75 percent was allocated to basic medical school funds and the remainder to the research and development accounts of the respective departments producing the funds.

As basic medical school support for the clinical departments was very limited during the 1950s departmental funds in the foundation were used primarily for small research projects and the cost of special training courses away from the institution for residents. In 1956, the general fund was used as collateral to borrow $255,000 for the construction of a house staff apartment building on the corner of Queen Street and Lockland Avenue. This facility was turned over to the hospital in 1959.

Dr. Richard G. Weaver, professor and director of the Section of Ophthalmology, was elected president of the foundation in 1967 and, because of his creative and even-handed financial and administrative skills, has served in that position since that time. Foundation assets in 1967 were $922,600, with an income for that year of $138,300, derived from interest on the corpus and professional fees. The hospital was serving as the collection agency but, as there was little incentive for carrying out this function, Weaver recommended the establishment of a separate unit for this purpose, reporting to the dean and advised by the Department of Clinics. This unit was to review patient records and bill for services on staff patients covered by private insurance. The foundation trustees accepted this suggestion, and collections increased rapidly from $90,000 to $300,000 per year. By 1983 the assets of the foundation had increased to $4 million, and income had reached $1,413,000.

The Medical Foundation has made many valuable contributions to the center. Between 1965 and 1970, a period during which hospital finances came under great pressure, $384,000 was allocated for house staff stipends and insurance, and $55,000 to strengthen hospital administration. Since that time funds have been used for major renovations of the house staff apartments, for the purchase of the Prudential Building to house behavioral science research programs and the Emeritus House on Hawthorne Road. Other major grants have been made for support of the medical center library, the computer center and the coronary care unit. Departmental funds have been used for pilot research projects, teaching equipment and enhancement of the training of house staff and fellows. Large contributions from the departments of Obstetrics and Gynecology and Surgery have established named professorships in those departments.

The Medical Foundation Clinical Teaching Scholar program was established in 1974 to strengthen the teaching program for residents and medical students. Under this program up to four young faculty members are selected each year and funds from the foundation provide salary support, which allows them to spend a major portion of their time in coordinated teaching and in discussions on medical education with senior administrative staff. Many of these scholars have continued to serve as outstanding members of the full-time faculty.

AFFILIATIONS BETWEEN THE MEDICAL SCHOOL AND VETERANS HOSPITALS

Following World War II the quality of medical care for veterans was increasingly criticized by veterans' organizations and the media. As a result, the Veterans Administration reorganized its medical care program in 1946 and established a policy that favored the affiliation of its hospitals with medical schools. The objective was to improve patient care and to become involved in graduate medical education. Affiliations were established through Dean's Committees, which were given the responsibility for the selection of the professional medical staff of the hospital, including interns and residents, and for supervising educational programs. Medical schools received no reimbursement for these services; however, faculty members serving as attending physicians or consultants were given individual stipends. A school could utilize the veterans hospital for the clinical training of its medical students if it so desired.

During 1946, the administration of the Mountain Home Veterans Hospital in Johnson City, Tennessee proposed an affiliation with Bowman Gray which included the development of three-year residency programs in general medicine and general surgery. However, the affiliation developed only as a consultant and lectureship arrangement due to the limited number of faculty at Bowman Gray at the time, and the 150-mile distance between the two institutions. This unofficial affiliation focused primarily on surgery, surgical pathology and laboratory medicine, and was discontinued in 1969.

During the early 1950s a similar relationship was developed between the Department of Surgery and the Veterans Hospital at Oteen, North Carolina, but ended when a proposed residency rotation did not materialize.

In an undated paper by Dr. Thomas T. Mackie, a former colonel in the Army and chairman of the Department of Preventive Medicine, it was indicated that three new veterans hospitals were to be built in North Carolina.[1] Hospitals in Oteen and Fayetteville were already open. The new hospitals included medical and surgical hospitals to be located near Duke Hospital and in Charlotte. The third, designated as a neuropsychiatric center, was to be located in Salisbury, North Carolina. Mackie made a strong case for locating the third hospital in Winston-Salem in association with Bowman Gray and a planned outpatient service for veterans in this city. He stated that he had discussed his proposal with the staff of the central office of the Veterans Administration and all agreed that, unless this happened, consultation and teaching services would remain very limited and sporadic at a Salisbury location. During further discussions on this matter, it became apparent that the designated location of the Veterans Hospital in Salisbury was the result of a promise made to Representative Robert Doughton of the Ninth District of North Carolina (that included this city) by President Franklin D. Roosevelt as a result of Doughton's support as chairman of the powerful Ways and Means Committee. Further, community attitudes toward a large neuropsychiatric hospital in Winston-Salem were divided, and Reid Holmes, the administrator of the Baptist Hospital, was strongly opposed because of the high competitive wages paid by the Veterans Administration to employees of these institutions. Coy Carpenter delayed the official opinion of the medical school, and finally replied to the inquiry in a neutral fashion. In the end, a 1,000-bed neuropsychiatric hospital was built in Salisbury and opened in December 1953.

Despite the concern of the Faculty Executive Council, a limited affiliation through a Dean's Committee was established between Bowman Gray and the Salisbury Veterans Hospital in January 1954. A representative of the Council on Medical Education and Hospitals of the American Medical Association urged that this be done in view of the high interest in the country at the time in improving the care of veterans. The affiliation began a faculty consultant relationship to assist in the postgraduate education of the hospital staff. It was hoped that this might lead to the development of a joint residency program in psychiatry and neurology. The residency program did not develop, and this led to a reappraisal of the relationship by the Faculty Executive Council in May 1962. The hospital was 35 miles away from the medical school and, though fully occupied, 98% of the patients had chronic neuropsychiatric problems. The full-time professional staff had an average age of 57, barely met minimum requirements, and young, well-qualified physicians expressed little interest in filling positions at the institution. It was concluded that the hospital provided no benefit to the medical school, and did not seem likely to do so in the future. Dr. James F. Toole, who joined the faculty shortly thereafter as chairman of the Department of Neurology, reviewed the situation and reached the same conclusion. As such, the Dean's Committee was terminated in April 1963, with a limited consultant relationship continuing for several years, as requested by the Salisbury hospital staff. However, several faculty members continue to serve as consultants to the veterans outpatient facility in Winston-Salem.

Many affiliations between medical schools and veterans hospitals in this country have been mutually beneficial and productive. However, the most successful relationships have developed with multispecialty veterans hospitals located in close geographic proximity to the affiliated medical schools.

1. Mackie, Thomas T., Location of Veterans Administration Hospitals (probably written in 1947 or 1948.)

DENOMINATIONAL RELATIONS AND PASTORAL CARE—
A BRIEF HISTORY
BY THE REV. CALVIN S. KNIGHT*

In the early years of Baptist Hospital there was a close tie between the hospital and the Baptist State Convention. This tie developed quite naturally from the pride which the churches had in the young institution they had birthed and from the hospital's dependence upon the churches for financial and moral support. Some of the most prominent Baptist leaders of the state served on the original hospital commission and on the first Board of Trustees which replaced the commission. A well-known Baptist pastor, the Rev. G.T. Lumpkin, was named the first "superintendent" of the hospital. Baptist churches, mostly through their Women's Missionary groups, were very much involved in raising funds for the hospital. All these factors contributed to the close relationship between the hospital and the convention.

Minutes of trustee meetings in the early years of the hospital indicate that the superintendent spent a good deal of his time working in the area of denominational relations. He traveled widely, often by bus, to attend Baptist associational meetings, to speak in Baptist churches and to represent Baptist Hospital at various denominational meetings. The purpose was to inform the Baptist people concerning the services, policies and procedures of the hospital and to solicit their prayers and gifts on behalf of the institution. Since the first hospital superintendent was a Baptist pastor, he also devoted part of his time to ministering to the spiritual needs of those who were patients in the hospital.

Trustee minutes clearly indicate that Mr. Smith Hagaman, who succeeded Mr. Lumpkin as superintendent, spent a great deal of his

*Director, Department of Church and Community Relations, North Carolina Baptist Hospital. This historical account extends through 1986.

time working in the area of denominational relations. Mr. Hagaman was a layman, and perhaps he did not feel as comfortable in making pastoral calls on patients as did his predecessor. At any rate, it was during Mr. Hagaman's tenure that the first steps were taken toward securing a person to serve as hospital chaplain. The board minutes of July 18, 1940, record, "Mr. Hagaman, the superintendent, reports that a Baptist layman has agreed to pay the salary of a resident minister at the hospital to administer [sic] to the spiritual needs of the patients and hospital force . . . and that it was his intention to make this provision permanent, all in accordance with the Board of Trustees of the hospital. Mr. E.L. Layfield moved that we accept the proposition and that the details of the plan be worked out by a committee, hereafter to be appointed." The motion was carried.

Trustee records do not specifically indicate the formal action of naming a hospital chaplain, perhaps because this action was an administrative matter. However, the July 29, 1943 minutes state, "It was moved by Mr. E.L. Davis and seconded by Rev. W.K. McGee that the agreement under which Rev. C.E. Parker was employed as hospital chaplain be spread upon the minutes." That motion was adopted. Appended to the minutes is a very formal document of agreement between Rev. C.E. Parker and Mr. C.M. Scott, the layman from High Point who had agreed to pay the salary of a "resident minister." Further, it is recorded that this agreement had been reached and the document signed almost three years earlier on September 20, 1940. Rev. Parker's work began on October 1, 1940, and his salary was $1,600 per year, paid in "equal weekly installments." Beginning September 1943, the trustee minutes regularly include reports from Rev. C.E. Parker "on the religious activities of the hospital."

The trustee minutes of November 4, 1943 record the election of Mr. Ray E. Brown as "administrator" of Baptist Hospital to commence on June 20, 1943. It was noted also that "Superintendent Smith Hagaman shall continue as superintendent of the hospital. He shall devote his time to the development of better relations between the hospital and the Baptist denomination; and shall seek to create stronger ties between Baptist churches and their members throughout the state and the hospital, including enlargement of the Mother's Day program. He shall also represent the hospital at denominational meetings of various kinds throughout the year including the Baptist State Convention, associational meetings and meetings of the various denominational boards and churches at which the Baptist Hospital shall be represented."

It is clear from other records that Superintendent Hagaman and Chaplain Parker shared in the responsibility and activities related to denominational relations. For example, trustee minutes of November 8, 1944, report that Superintendent Hagaman had attended thirty-two Baptist associational meetings across the state, traveling on the average 182 miles mostly by bus and that Chaplain Parker had attended eighteen associational meetings for that season. It was noted also that, together, they had attended fifty of the seventy associations or approximately eighty percent of the total.

At the April 24, 1945 meeting of the trustees, it is reported that "a long and detailed discussion" was held regarding the position of Director of Religious Activities. It was apparent in the discussion that the board was not ready at this time to make a permanent appointment to this position. The final decision was summed up in the motion made by Dr. W.K. McGee, seconded by Mr. O.M. Mull: "Be it resolved that a committee be appointed by the president of the board to recommend by the first of January 1946 a person for the position of Director of Religious Activities and Denominational Relations. It is further moved that until such time as the board appoints such a person that Mr. Charles E. Parker be continued as chaplain and that he be placed on a full-time basis during the period." This motion was passed unanimously.

These same minutes refer to a resolution passed in the January 1945 meeting of the trustees which recommended that the chairman of the board appoint a "Religious Committee," consisting of three trustees, two of whom shall be pastors. The duties of this committee were "to work with the hospital organization for an enlarged emphasis on the religious program." The president appointed the following trustees to serve on the committee: Dr. W.K. McGee, Dr. B.A. Bowers, and Mrs. Otis Tucker. The president of the board also named the following local ministers to serve as an advisory committee to work with the trustee committee: Rev. J.M. Hayes, chairman; Dr. Ralph A. Herring; Mr. M.L. Mott; and Rev. M.A. Adams.

Attached to these minutes is a memorandum dated April 25, 1945, implementing a resolution of the Board of Trustees passed on January 30, 1945, which merges the duties of the Office of Chaplain with the Office of Denominational Representative. It states that Mr. Parker will head the work of this department until a permanent appointment is made.

The memorandum goes on to state that the director shall be

responsible for a Program of religious activities for employees and student nurses, including vespers and chapel services and periodic Religious Emphasis Weeks; for regular visitation of hospital patients as well as being on call for emergency care; for serving as liaison between patients and hometown pastors; for being available for special conferences with patients; for editing *Baptist Hospital News* and a special page to be mailed from the W.M.U. headquarters in Raleigh, both quarterlies; for preparing all literature to promote the Mother's Day offering, for speaking in churches, attending associational meetings and other denominational meetings; for generally serving as the liaison between the hospital and the pastors/churches; for teaching a course in Bible to student nurses; and for general support of the hospital's programs. The director also will be responsible for hearing complaints and suggestions from patients and communicating with the appropriate staff members in trying to resolve these problems.

The memorandum also outlines the manner in which the new Department of Religious Activities will fit into the overall departmental organization of the hospital.

Meanwhile, the committee appointed to recommend a chaplain and director of Religious Activities, under the chairmanship of Dr. W.K. McGee, was holding regular meetings. On June 7, 1945, the committee voted to extend an invitation to the Rev. Edwin F. Perry of Rockingham to visit the medical center and meet with the committee. On June 29, 1945, the committee met to discuss the memorandum outlining the duties and relationships of the director of Religious Activities. After lengthy discussion and a few minor amendments, the committee voted its approval of this memorandum. The committee met on July 31, 1945, and Dr. McGee reported that Mr. Perry had declined the invitation to consider the position. In this same meeting, the committee requested that Dr. McGee and the trustee chairman investigate the qualifications for a Mr. Paul Crandal and a Dr. Tyler to see if either would be interested in the position.

At the meeting of the trustees on the same day Dr. McGee reported that his committee would need time to make further investigation before it could recommend a person as director of Religious Activities. Chaplain Parker reported that Miss Daphne Penny had been employed as student secretary. Her primary responsibility would be to direct religious activities for students and employees.

On September 11, 1945 the committee to recommend a chaplain and Religious Director met to hear a report that Dr. Olin T. Binkley of the Southern Baptist Theological Seminary in Louisville had been contacted to determine whether he would be interested in the position. Dr. Binkley had replied that he felt compelled to remain in the field of religious education. Whereupon, a motion was approved to retain the Rev. C.E. Parker as chaplain for the remainder of the year and through 1946 and that the search for a Religious Director be continued. A motion was passed to invite Dr. W.C. Tyler to visit the hospital at hospital expense, presumably for the purpose of considering this position.

The administrator's report to the Trustees dated September 30, 1945, defines the duties of the Department of Religion and Denomination Affairs. This statement is essentially the same as the job description outlined in the April 25, 1945, memorandum mentioned earlier.

At the trustee meeting October 23, 1945 Mr. Ray Brown, who had recently resigned as aministrator of the hospital, was present and presented a proposal for organizing the Department of Religion and Denominational Activities. This plan had previously been approved by the Baptist ministers of Winston-Salem and was unanimously approved by the trustees.

Later in that same meeting, Dr. W.K. McGee "modestly retired from the meeting," and Mrs. J.C. Turner, a member of the committee to find a director of Religion and Denominational Activities, reported that their committee had concluded after long and careful consideration that the person best suited for this position was Dr. W.K. McGee. She recommended that Dr. McGee be employed for the position and that his services commence not later than January 1, 1946, if possible. Mr. C.M. Scott seconded the motion, and it was unanimously approved. Dr. McGee returned to the meeting and, upon being informed of this vote, expressed his appreciation for the consideration. He did not indicate at this point whether he would accept the invitation.

However, the trustee minutes for January 29, 1946 record that "Religious Director Dr. W.K. McGee" submitted a report on the activities of his department. The report appended to these minutes states that Dr. McGee began his duties on December 1, 1945 and gives an account of some of the activities in which he had been involved since assuming office. It indicated that already he was feeling some tension between his responsibility as chaplain to patients on the one hand and his responsibility for denominational relations on the other. He states that this tension is felt more keenly because of the unexpected resignation of Rev. Charles E. Parker, the chaplain, to accept a pastorate in Franklin, North Carolina. The report states further that Dr. McGee's hope is that this vacancy can soon be filled since there is need to have "at least one person in the hospital at all times during the day and on-call through the night available for any special call that might come." He indicates that it is not possible for one person to do this and meet all of the out-of-town engagements in churches and associations.

In the minutes of May 7, 1946, Dr. McGee's report to the board states that, although he is now making regular rounds with patients, he still feels the frustration of not being able to give adequate time to patient ministries, especially to counseling with those who have special needs. Dr. McGee reported also that consideration was being given to the possibilities of training young ministerial students in the hospital ministry.

Trustee records do not give details of the process for employing Richard K. Young, but minutes for the meeting for October 22, 1946 state that "the proposed annual report of the hospital Board of Trustees to the State Convention was submitted for consideration. Special emphasis was given to the Department of Religion under the direction of Dr. W.K. McGee and assisted by the Rev. Richard K. Young." Dr. McGee was not present for this meeting, and there was no report from his department.

Dr. McGee's statement to the trustees on January 24, 1947 speaks of the work being done by the associate director and of the need for a secretary to assist the director and the assistant director.

The next reference in the trustee minutes to Dr. Young's work occurs in the April 22, 1947 minutes. Dr. McGee's report to this meeting showed that "Mr. Young's activities to a large extent had been directed to the preparation for the program of clinical training this summer, and it was noted that five men, one undergraduate and four graduates, were to take their training from July 1 to September 5." The same minutes record that there was discussion about the need for a staff person "specially qualified" in the area of public relations to help improve "the attitude among members of the denomination" toward the hospital and the medical school. The trustees voted to authorize the Executive Committee to study this matter and to "take such steps as might be necessary in the employment of a competent person to handle this."

These minutes reflected also the resignation of Mrs. Daphne Penny

184

Stanton who had recently married. Miss Edith Arrington of Florida was to succeed Mrs. Stanton on June 1, 1947, as student secretary in the department.

In his report to the trustees on July 22, 1947 Dr. McGee stated that he expected to attend practically all of the associations this year. He said that student work was going well under the leadership of Miss Arrington and the Clinical Pastoral Training program was "progressing nicely" under the leadership of Mr. Young. In November of that year Dr. McGee reported that plans for a six-week course in clinical pastoral training for pastors would be offered in January and February. This course would be less technical than the course offered in the summer. In April of the following year, Dr. McGee reported that "five Negro pastors" had participated in the clinical training program under Mr. Young, doing their hospital visitation at Kate Bitting Hospital.

In July of 1948, Dr. McGee reported to the trustees that Mr. Young had been granted a leave of absence to work on his doctorate and that his work would be carried on by Mr. O.W. Rhodenhiser, an assistant chaplain on the staff. No mention is made in the minutes of Dr. Young's return to the hospital until December 20, 1949, when he is listed among those present for a special board meeting.

At the trustee meeting for January 25, 1951 it was brought to the attention of the board that the faculty of the Bowman Gray School of Medicine had voted Dr. W.K. McGee as the most valuable member of the faculty during 1949-1950.

Dr. McGee's report to the trustees a year later states, "Richard K. Young has just completed his thesis for a doctorate, and the Southern Baptist Seminary has requested permission to publish the thesis." Dr. McGee went on to say that the Clinical Pastoral Training program is becoming recognized as the finest of its kind in the country and that there are from one to three chaplains in training under Dr. Young's leadership at all times.

Dr. McGee's annual report to the board in January 1952 states that Miss Marjorie Joyner of Winston-Salem, a graduate of Meredith College, had succeeded Mrs. Edith Arrington Lineback as student secretary in July. He indicated further that many students, both nursing and medical, were participating in religious activities. He also reported that Miss Joyner teaches Bible and Dr. Young teaches Psychology to the student nurses.

In January 1951 it was noted that Chaplain Everette Barnard, previously a resident in Pastoral Care, had returned from the Missouri Baptist Hospital in St. Louis to serve as a chaplain, dividing his time between Baptist Hospital and Graylyn (Psychiatric Center). With this addition, the department had two assistant residents and one fellowship, the latter made possible by a gift from the Atlas Supply Company of which Mr. E.L. Davis, Jr., was president.

Dr. McGee reported that the 1951 Mother's Day offering amounted to $157,000, a 12% increase over the previous year; indicated that he had attended seventy-three annual associational meetings and had spoken in numerous churches and other denominational meetings. The Mother's Day offering for 1952 was $165,000.

Dr. McGee's annual report for 1952 states that Miss Ruth Swan was the new student secretary succeeding Mrs. Marjorie Joyner Northrup, who had become secretary to Dr. Richard Young. Miss Swan, a native of Statesville, graduated from Mars Hill College, Blue Mountain College, North Carolina Baptist Hospital's School of Nursing and the W.M.U. Training School in Louisville, Kentucky. She had served a year as a missionary in Lebanon.

A proposal for dividing the Department of Religion into two departments is attached to the trustee minutes for January 29, 1953, and, presumably, was adopted to become effective at about that time. A preface to the proposal states that the work of the Department of Religion has grown both in the area of pastoral ministry to patients and in the area of denominational relations so that there is "need for the separation and strengthening of these phases of work in the religious field." The proposal was to create a Department of Denominational Activities with Dr. W.K. McGee as the director, and a Department of Religious Activities with Dr. Richard K. Young as the director.

The Department of Denominational Activities would be responsible for promoting the Mother's Day offering and would also be involved in general fund raising for the institution, especially as related to capital expansion programs. The department would also seek to maintain and strengthen relationships with the churches of the Baptist State Convention through speaking engagements in the churches and in denominational meetings, as well as strengthening public relations in general through appearances in civic clubs, schools, ministerial conferences, and other gatherings. The department would continue to communicate with pastors and others regarding patient appointments, admissions to the hospital, financial arrangements for hospital bills and other matters.

The Department of Religious Activities would be responsible for providing a pastoral ministry to patients, for offering courses in pastoral care at various levels to ministers, seminary students and other religious workers and for offering counseling to students, medical center personnel, ministers and others. It would also supervise the worship services in the chapel.

The proposal also suggests that an advisory committee be appointed for the two departments consisting of the trustee chairman, the chairman of the Finance Committee, the hospital administrator and the two department directors.

Following the separation of the two departments, Dr. McGee continued as director of Denominational Relations for many years, tirelessly and enthusiastically performing whatever specific tasks seemed necessary and appropriate to fulfill the general purposes of his office. He crisscrossed the state in his travels, driving hundreds of thousands of miles, speaking in churches and denominational meetings for the purpose of imparting information about and establishing good will for the Baptist Hospital. He was instrumental in setting up a network of Baptist Hospital representatives, one in each of the seventy-plus Baptist associations in the state. These representatives served as liaison for the hospital with the Baptist people in each community.

Dr. McGee also conceived the idea and carried out the plan for establishing what he called the Service Patient Endowment Fund. These funds were to be invested, and the interest earned was to supplement offerings from Baptist churches used to assist financially needy patients with their hospital bills. This fund was started in June of 1956 with an initial grant of $1,000. Through the years very few gifts have exceeded this in size, but numerous contributions made in honor, or in memory, of some person have added up to a significant total. In 1980, members of Dr. McGee's family honored him on his eightieth birthday by making additional significant contributions to this fund. At that time, upon recommendation of the hospital's administrative staff, the trustees voted to rename the fund "The W.K. McGee Patient Endowment Fund." In 1986, the fund totalled $564,534.

In early 1970, Dr. McGee contacted the Rev. Calvin Knight, then pastor of the Weldon Baptist Church in Weldon and a trustee of the hospital, to ask if he would consider coming to work as his associate with a view to succeeding him when he retired. Mr. Knight assumed the position of associate director of Denominational Relations in June of 1970 and a year later was named department director.

Dr. McGee continued as the associate director until April of the following year when he retired. He was active in church and denominational life as well as in community affairs until his sudden death in June of 1983.

The Department of Denominational Relations changed its name in 1976 to Church and Community Relations, a name which seemed to reflect more accurately the functions of the office. The office serves as liaison for the hospital with the public in general, but the main thrust of its work continues to be that of strengthening the ties between the hospital and the churches, especially the churches of the Baptist State Convention. At this writing the hospital enjoys an excellent relationship with the Baptist churches. One evidence of this is the fact that in fiscal year 1986 these churches gave through the Cooperative Program and the special offering a total of $1,083,051, the largest amount for the hospital's ministry that has been given in any single year of its history.

HISTORY OF THE DEPARTMENT OF PASTORAL CARE
BY THE REVEREND L.L. MCGEE*

The Department and School of Pastoral Care of the North Carolina Baptist Hospitals, Inc., is the oldest chaplaincy program in the South to provide a ministry to patients, families, medical staff, and education to pastors and theological students. It is known as one of the largest departments with a faculty of fifteen, three associate staff, and eleven secretarial staff.

Ministries to patients, families, and medical staff have averaged 50,834 in the last five years. Out-patient pastoral counseling reached 21,724 hours in 1986. In the last forty years there have been 2,222 students enrolled in various programs of pastoral education. The students are made up of pastors, theological students, and others in church-related programs. Students were from 39 countries and represented 39 different denominations.

The department has played a major role in reflecting the spirit of the medical center in seeking to actualize the healing ministry of Jesus; taking seriously the treatment of the mind, body, and spirit. It has been a major contributor in the development of the holistic concept of the delivery of health care.

The roots of the department are visible in the early concern of the hospital for not only the physical welfare of patients but also the spiritual. The hospital was mindful of the spiritual needs of persons experiencing illness. A part-time chaplain, Charles E. Parker, was employed in 1943. In two years he was full-time until Dr. W.K. McGee was appointed director of the Department of Religion and Denominational Activities to begin his duties in December 1945.

The job description for the new director included visiting patients,

*Director, Division of Clinical Pastoral Education, Department of Pastoral Care, North Carolina Baptist Hospital. This historical account extends through 1986.

their families, counseling, functioning as a liaison person between the hospital and churches in the North Carolina Baptist State Convention. McGee sought and recommended the employment of Dr. Richard K. Young as the associate director in the Department of Religion in 1946.

The hospital was beginning to move from a general hospital to a referral teaching institution. There was recognition of the need for expansion, and it became a leading treatment center. This movement reflected in the establishment and growth of the Department of Pastoral Care.

Prior to becoming chaplain, Richard K. Young was at Southern Baptist Theological Seminary where the insights of psychology and behavioral science were being correlated with theological understandings. These relatively new dynamics to ministry had potential for enhancing the effectiveness of pastoral care and counseling. Young also had received clinical training at Elgin State Mental Hospital in Elgin, Illinois. Here he had first-hand knowledge in the study of the "living human documents"[1] as a way of preparing oneself for education. This training, now known as Clinical Pastoral Education (CPE), was started in 1925 by Anton T. Boisen at Worcester State Hospital, Worcester, Massachusetts. CPE is a distinctive learning approach in theological education. It is a form of experimental learning in actual pastoral functioning. The minister explores and evaluates relevant forms of ministry with his peers and supervisor. Not only does a minister improve his professional skills and develop new resources for ministry, but the minister develops a clearer understanding of himself in relationship to others, which enables him to evaluate and enhance his ministry. It was an invaluable learning experience for Young, and he was committed to providing clinical pastoral education—of blending service and education. The hospital was seeking to fill a chaplaincy position with a minister who could actualize an informed ministry to patients and others while teaching pastors and staff in the process.

The first class of theological students occurred in the summer of 1947. These students, along with their professor, Dr. Wayne Oates, came from the Southern Baptist Theological Seminary where Young had recently graduated. The curriculum included daily didactic sessions, case histories, assigned reading, as well as techniques and methods for ministering to particular patients. This was all correlated with a heavy emphasis on patient ministry where students were assigned to certain services in the hospital and became the chaplain to those patients. The clinical practice of pastoral care was closely supervised by Young and Oates. This was the first program of Clinical Pastoral Education in the south.

Young did a survey to determine whether or not the original mission of Southern Baptists in establishing institutional ministries to the sick was being accomplished.[2] Young wanted to know how close the Baptist hospitals were holding to their original purposes stated as: 1) to give medical care to the poor; 2) carry out the healing ministry of Jesus; 3) to train women in the field of nursing, and 4) to furnish an avenue of service to nurses and doctors who feel the Christian call. Twenty-six hospitals were surveyed, and Young reported in his thesis the following:

1. These hospitals as a whole are not performing a religious ministry in keeping with the purpose for which they were established.

2. It is clear that the weakest point in the hospital set-up is found in the failure to place more emphasis upon cementing a better relationship between the hospital and the denomination.

3. Baptists need very badly to capture the spirit of the medical missionary hospital on the foreign field and incorporate it into many of these hospitals on the home front.[3]

These findings certainly influenced Young in his own ministry, as well as the efforts he put into the development of the Department of Pastoral Care.

Young taught courses to nurses, and in 1948 was asked by Dr. C.C. Carpenter, dean of the Bowman Gray School of Medicine, to teach medical students about the relationship between religion and medicine. His acceptance and status were growing in the hospital medical center as well as in the community, state, and nation.

The Rev. Everett Barnard, who was a member of the first class of 1947, and O.W. Rhodenhiser, former seminary classmate, came on the staff as assistant chaplains. It was during 1948 that Young returned to Southern Baptist Theological Seminary in Louisville, Kentucky, to complete his Doctor of Theology degree. Young's dissertation resulted in his first book, *The Pastor's Hospital Ministry*, viewed by many as creative and innovative.

There was little to inform pastors about hospital ministry. Few hospital chaplains had been trained for their specialized ministry. The Rev. Joe Fred Luck was the chaplain at Memorial Baptist Hospital in Houston, Texas. He was one of the few who knew the value of specialized training for service as a hospital chaplain. As colleagues,

Luck and Young made a pact. Luck would do the legwork for Young to do workshops in the south for upgrading the training of those who were serving as hospital chaplains in Baptist hospitals and for the pastor's hospital ministry.[4]

In 1952 a two-week clinic especially for hospital chaplains was held at the North Carolina Baptist Hospital. Enrolled in this clinic were chaplains from thirteen hospitals across the south. It was referred to as the "first hospital chaplain's institute ever held in the south." The department has led the way in advocating training of ministers as hospital chaplains, as well as pioneered the use of pastoral care in hospitals and the training of pastors for the specialization as hospital chaplains.

These were busy days for Richard K. Young and the staff of Everett Barnard and O.W. Rhodenhiser. They had earned the respect of the medical center, other academic institutions, North Carolina Baptists, as well as those of other denominations. The department has been ecumenical from the beginning.

Wake Forest College, Young's alma mater, requested cooperation from the department to work with students enrolled through the Bowman Gray School of Medicine, and Southeastern Baptist Theological Seminary requested an academic connection with the clinical training program so that students could have on-the-job experience in a general hospital setting. To solidify this connection and to fill the young seminary's need for a program instruction, Dr. Sydnor L. Stealey, president of Southeastern, in 1952 invited Young to become its first professor of Pastoral Care.

During 1953 another first occurred. Right on the heels of the institute for hospital chaplains came a three-day institute on pastoral care sponsored by Bowman Gray and Baptist Hospital. The *Twin City Sentinel* referred to it as the "first of its type in the south." Dr. Helen Flanders Dunbar, professor at Columbia University's School of Medicine, was to be the keynote speaker. She was considered an authority on the relationship between emotional problems and physical illness, which of course was of special interest to Young and part of the didactic presentations designed to enhance the ministry and understanding of pastors. Dunbar was unable to attend due to illness, but the medical perspective was contributed by Drs. Wingate Johnson, Manson Meads, Lloyd J. Thompson, and Angus Randolph, all of Bowman Gray School of Medicine. The institute was attended by 375 pastors from all over the south. This type of continuing education for pastors met a significant need; it was new, exciting, and provided tremendous insights for ministry.

Dr. D. Swan Haworth, who was serving as pastor of the First Baptist Church in Lumberton, North Carolina (and who later became director of the Pastoral Counseling Division), gave this account to the *Biblical Recorder*:

> Just imagine getting to listen to lectures by doctors, sociologists, hospital chaplains, pastors, psychiatrists, etc. And more than that, imagine getting to ask them questions which you definitely need to have answered in order to perform a more effective ministry among those whom God has entrusted to your care. That was the experience of some 300 pastors who attended this institute, the first of its kind to be held in our state.

In 1953 the board of trustees of the North Carolina Baptist Hospital granted a request from Richard K. Young to become a separate department created under his directorship called the Department of Religious Activities. W.K. McGee reported in January 1953, at a quarterly meeting of the board of trustees of the North Carolina Baptist Hospital that 5,000 visits had been made to patients for health and welfare. Baptist ministers and hospital people from all over are "clamoring to enroll in courses of study offered by the department, and the field of pastoral care is assuming major proportions. The work being done by Dr. Young and his staff is outstanding in the nation."

A recommendation made by the administrator, Mr. Reid Holmes, reads:

> The work of the Department of Religion has progressed under the able leadership of Dr. W.K. McGee to embrace such a wide scope of activity that it is deemed wise to divide the responsibility of this department into two departments. One of these departments is to be known as the Department of Denominational Activities, headed by Dr. W.K. McGee, and the other is to be known as the Department of Religious Activities, headed by Dr. Richard K. Young.[5]

Meredith Neill[6] states this recommendation came as a surprise to Dr. W.K. McGee; however, he was not opposed to the division. McGee and Young were entrepreneurs and needed to reconstruct the department to accommodate needed growth and development.

193

By the second report to the trustees in 1953, the words "Pastoral Care" are substituted for "Religious Activities." This name change on the part of the department was more descriptive and in keeping with the nomenclature for the work of chaplains and educators.

The Department of Pastoral Care sought not only to respond to the needs of patients, their families, and medical personnel, but was very sensitive in providing institutes and educational opportunities to meet the needs of pastors who often indicated that their former theological education had not prepared them properly to function in their role as pastors. Hundreds of pastors sought admission in the various short-term educational opportunities known as the six-weeks course. As Dr. Young used to say, "This program was designed to knock off some of the rough edges as far as personal idiosyncrasies that impair full use of one's self as a minister." This was always done in a pastoral climate whereby the doctrine of grace and koininia (community of understanding and acceptance) were experienced in small groups and communicated by clinical theological educators. This mix of understanding others by understanding yourself was very powerful and led to the increased competency and effectiveness of ministers throughout the nation and many parts of the world.

There was a significant period of expansion after 1953 with new staff members being added and areas of work deepened. The Chaplain to Students program, especially designed to respond to the needs of medical students, was formed with Ms. Margaret Pearson being the first to hold this position. Other new staff added to meet the needs of the institution for service and education were: Dr. Kenneth Pepper, the Rev. Dean Bergen, and the Rev. Arnold Smith.

The Davis Memorial Chapel, which began as an idea by the Egbert Davis family in 1943, reached completion in 1954. A gift from the Atlas Supply Company, owned by the Davis family, made this chapel possible. It was erected in memory of Mrs. Annie Pearl Shore Davis and in honor of Mr. Egbert Davis, Sr., both of whom participated in the early beginnings of the hospital. Mrs. Davis was well known for the pastoral care she provided in delivering flowers from the family garden to patients. Her son, Mr. Egbert Davis, Jr., said there were times when his mother was "barely visible in the car for all the flowers."[7] The Davis Memorial Chapel was a blessing to all, and the chapel basement provided space for the School of Pastoral Care.

The Department of Pastoral Care experienced significant growth of personnel and programs during the seven-year period after its establishment which paralleled the expansion of the hospital and medical school. The earliest fund raising drive by the alumni of the School of Pastoral Care resulted in the purchase of the St. John's Lutheran Church property which provided additional office and classroom facilities.

The pastoral counseling service needed the Rev. Benjamin S. Patrick, who was employed as director of the pastoral counseling services. The Rev. George Colgin came in 1956 and supervised patient ministries. During 1957-1962 he coordinated clinical pastoral education with medical students and CPE residents, having joint classes with the medical school Department of Preventive Medicine. One of the first actualizations of the goal of the American Medical Association was realized as student chaplains, known as Residents in CPE, and medical residents presented patients and came to more fully understand their role in the care of individual patients. They made rounds together.

Colgin also initiated the idea of having alumni of the School of Pastoral Care. He helped plan the first institute, as well as the first alumni newsletter, later to be known as *The Verbatim*.

Dr. Albert L. Meiburg was employed primarily to do research in the growing discipline of pastoral care and counseling. The Rev. Robert F. Gunter also joined the staff for the year 1959-1960. The Rev. Herbert Zerof became a staff member in 1960 and remained until 1963.

The article entitled, "Out-Patient Pastoral Counseling in a Medical Center," was co-authored by Young and Patrick. This article was published in *The Journal of the American Medical Association*, and caught the attention of Dr. Clarence Hall, senior editor of the Reader's Digest. Hall commissioned Young to produce "a condensed book" for the Reader's Digest in September 1959, entitled, "Spiritual Therapy: Modern Medicine's Newest Ally." This was the first time a condensed book came before the final book was written entitled, *Spiritual Therapy*, co-authored by Young and Meiburg in 1960.

In the 1960 annual report to trustees we read:

> The public relations emphasis of the past two years have enhanced the work of the department with public interest far beyond anything we had contemplated. The demands for clinical training resulting from this have forced us to determine our maximum faculty-student ratio and evaluate the capacity of our present clinical facilities for training. During 1960 our classes filled up as much as nine months in advance.[8]

195

A film was also produced by the department entitled, "A Guide to Hospital Visitation." This film was widely circulated for pastoral study groups. In the following year, a half-hour documentary was made by the National Broadcasting Company in conjunction with the Radio and Television Commission of the Southern Baptist Convention entitled, "From the Most High Cometh Healing." This featured the work of the Department of Pastoral Care in the hospital and showed one of the staff members, Herbert Zerof, ministering to a patient.

The Department of Pastoral Care was well recognized both for its service and education. Mr. Reid Holmes, the administrator, comments on this fact in a report to the trustees on October 26, 1961. He said:

> At the American Hospital Association convention there was a group for hospital chaplains. The Rev. Granger Westberg of the University of Chicago Clinics, one of the speakers of the session, had commented that the finest school in hospital chaplaincy is at the Baptist Hospital, Winston-Salem, North Carolina.[9]

Reid Holmes saw the value of the chaplains in ministry to patients not only to care for their spiritual needs but to service their other needs similar to social workers. It was for this reason that for many years there were no social workers on the staff of the hospital due to the staff chaplain supervisors and student chaplains. The department was also involved in a Church-Hospital-Family Service that provided meals and lodging for needy families of patients and medications for indigent patients being discharged. This service continues today under the direction of Chaplain George Bowman.

The Committee for a Model Community program came into being in 1961 when Mr. Charles H. Babcock, a partner of Reynolds and Company, reportedly had a dream about the availability of people in the community to help the needy. He called Mr. Marshall C. Kurfees, former Winston-Salem mayor, stating that since the United Fund Drive had been so successful and revealed the availability of so many people who wished to become involved in the rehabilitative assistance of the community's less fortunate, he would like to set up a Model Community. Kurfees agreed to be the director and sought the services of Dr. Richard K. Young to assist him in the establishment of a Committee for a Model Community.[10]

The Model Community under the leadership of Kurfees established the "Meals on Wheels" for persons who were on special diets and unable to prepare their own food, the Each One Teach One program to address the literacy problem of many citizens, and scholarships for student chaplains to minister to persons in other community institutions, such as Goodwill Industries and Juvenile Detention. Training was offered to laypersons who wanted to function as lay counselors in their neighborhoods.

During this period, Wesley E. Brett, who had been a former intern and resident, joined the staff as a coordinator of the Church-Hospital-Family Service. He is presently the director for administration of the Department of Pastoral Care. The Chaplain to Students' position was filled by the Rev. Everett Gill in 1961, the Rev. Lowell Sodeman (1964-1966), the Rev. Charles F. Wilson (1967-1976), the Rev. Baxter Wynn part-time 1976-1979), and Dr. S. Bryant Kendrick (1979-1986).

Also in 1962, personal illness claimed the services of Richard K. Young. He was hospitalized for two months of psychiatric observation and treatment. The local newspaper carried this story quoting Young's personal physician in saying, "Nationally prominent minister and author is being treated for chronic depression, as Young had been in a state of depression for the past year or more."[11]

The news of Young's illness was dealt with compassionately by the community at large. In fact, the response of the community was the way Young had taught his students to respond to others in similar difficulties. During his hospitalization he wrote a very significant letter to the editor of the *Twin City Sentinel:*

Unless one has descended into the lower regions of despondency and depression, where all is lost and there remains only a feeling of total rejection when one has attempted to destroy oneself, then and then only, can one understand the difficulty I am experiencing in trying to impart to you with mere words my profound appreciation for your editorial.

Somehow you realized that the Dick Young riding down the highway that day was not the Dick Young people had come to know in the past. Knowing you arrived at your conclusion without any knowledge of the facts in the case has caused me, without a doubt, to experience the love and understanding that can only come through the "pure grace of God."[12]

During Young's sick leave the department was ably led by Dr. Albert . Meiburg and the staff that included Brett, Patrick, and Zerof. For the next two years the work of the Model Community became even more integrated with the educational activities of the Department of Pastoral Care. Offices were integrated with those of the department, and Kenneth A. Burnette joined the staff as an instructor and coordinator with the Model Community. At the end of 1963 the school had provided training for 894 ministers and religious workers from 37 states, 23 foreign countries (10 of these being nationals), and representing 31 denominations.

If the first ten years were to be seen as establishment and development, the next ten years in the history of the Department of Pastoral Care can be characterized as time of consolidating gains, continued expansion, and enhancing relationships with academic institutions and the North Carolina Baptist State Convention. To provide some of these services Young departed from his policy of employing primarily those whom he had personally trained. As an assistant director in charge of curriculum, supervising students, and counseling, he sought the employ of L.L. McGee, who had trained at the Institute of Religion in Houston, Texas, and was serving as the secretary of the Hospital Chaplaincy of the Chaplains Commission of the Home Mission Board of the Southern Baptist Convention. McGee is currently director of the Division of Clinical Pastoral Education.

The Rev. Richard W. McKay, who had been serving as chaplain in a state mental hospital in Marion, Virginia, was employed in 1964 as chaplain supervisor; the Rev. George W. Bowman, III, who had been pastor in South Boston, Virginia, joined the staff in 1966, bringing with him his expertise as a writer, having published *Sermons for the Junior Congregation*, and was to later produce another book, *The Dynamic of Confession*. He was the first president of Hospice of Winston-Salem, Forsyth County, Inc., and is presently serving as director for hospital ministry.

The Rev. Maurice Briggs joined the staff in 1966 as director of urban ministries, being closely integrated with the Model Community program. He serves as chaplain supervisor and chairs the admissions committee of the Division of Clinical Pastoral Education.

The quality of the curriculum was recognized by the United States Air Force, and the School of Pastoral Care was selected as one of two approved clinical pastoral education centers in the country. A contract was entered into with the United States Air Force, and three different classes for Air Force chaplains, many of whom had served in Vietnam, were held with ten in each class. The Air Force saw this as an opportunity to help returning chaplains from Vietnam with re-entry to home and country.

In 1967 the hospital and the programs of Clinical Pastoral Education were accredited by the Association for Clinical Pastoral Education, Inc. It was accredited to offer three levels of training: basic, advanced, and supervisory. That accreditation has been maintained with a review in 1974.

A few years after the purchase of the Lutheran Church on Queen Street, the hospital was expanding and needed parking space. The building was torn down. Student housing was relocated in the Kembly Inn Motel building, which at that time was at the corner of Cloverdale and Medical Center Boulevard. This building was also replaced with a parking lot, and students in the department were given housing in Twin Castles Apartments. When these were removed due to further expansion, a house on Queen Street was designated for student housing.

In May of 1970 Young accepted early retirement for health reasons. He did continue to write and teach through the North Carolina Memorial Hospital in Chapel Hill. In April of 1971 he returned to his hometown community of Roxboro, North Carolina. There he was welcomed enthusiastically and did pastoral counseling in his home, worked on a manuscript on dream center therapy, and held an interim pastorate until his death in December 1974. Two months after his death the Department of Pastoral Care and the hospital paid him high tribute at the 1975 Alumni Institute. In this service Young was described as "a pioneer in pastoral care, pastoral psychology, and clinical pastoral chaplaincy and education. His story was also the story of the development of the Department of Pastoral Care of the North Carolina Baptist Hospital."[13]

The coming of Dr. John E. Lynch as executive vice president of the North Carolina Baptist Hospitals, Inc., in 1970 and his promotion in 1972 to chief executive officer has been very significant in the life, growth, and development of the Department of Pastoral Care. His support through the years has been an enabling factor in the continued programs of the department.

Under the leadership of Dr. Andrew D. Lester (1971-1976) the department was reorganized. Two divisions were formed: 1) the Division of Clinical Pastoral Education under the direction of Chaplain L.L. McGee, and 2) the Division of Pastoral Counseling under the direction of Dr. Swan Haworth, who had joined the staff earlier as a pastoral counselor. Dr. Haworth had been for a number of years professor in the Department of Psychology of Religion at Southern Baptist Theological Seminary.

Some of the highlights of the department during this time include: the establishment of a Master's degree program in pastoral counseling at Wake Forest University; increased participation and service by staff members in the professional organization of the Association for Clinical Pastoral Education, Inc. Staff members were elected to key positions reflecting the Association's appreciation for the quality of ministry and education being conducted at the Department and/or School of Pastoral Care. L.L. McGee served as chairman of the certification committee, as well as regional chairperson; Wesley Brett served as treasurer; George Bowman served as treasurer, and as member of Research, of Certification, and of Accreditation Committees; and Maurice Briggs was later to become regional director on a part-time basis of the Mid-Atlantic Region.

In 1973 another division of the department was formed called Human Enrichment and Development (HED). Dr. M. Mahan Siler, whose background and training especially qualified him, became the first director. The development of the HED program was another first for the department in emphasizing prevention of illness in the ministry of pastoral care.

The demands for counseling through the Division of Pastoral Counseling continued to grow. Dr. Ted Dougherty was employed as a pastoral counselor, and serves presently as director of that Division. Later, in 1982, Dr. Daniel Jungkuntz joined the pastoral counseling staff and is presently director of the pastoral counseling training program.

In 1972 a Committee of Fifteen was appointed by the North Carolina Baptist State Convention to review the relationship of the hospital to the convention. Statements from the study indicate a vital connection between North Carolina Baptists and the Department of Pastoral Care. From a lengthy study the committee reported the following:

> . . . North Carolina Baptists are seeking to demonstrate the sensitivity of Jesus in the halls of North Carolina Baptist Hospital. . . . The Christian view of death and the Christian hope of immortality, an immortality based on the resurrection of Christ, are not to be left to the chance

that the patient will happen to have a doctor or nurse who holds these views. Built into the total healing ministry of North Carolina Baptist Hospital should be the availability of this hope to those unfortunate who cannot be healed. The School of Pastoral Care is on the premises. The staff of the School of Pastoral Care is willing to make a Christian ministry available to those who must die.[14]

Other statements from the study include:

. . . Once again the School of Pastoral Care has something to say to sick people. The time of introspection that serious illness affords is also a time for openness to the counsel the Christian religion offers.[15]

And the final statement was:

We believe the School of Pastoral Care has fulfilled an important function in the past and deserves the full support of the hospital administration, trustees, and the Baptist State Convention in the future. We recommend to the trustees of the hospital that the Pastoral Care School be given full status as a vital part of the service and care of the Baptist Hospital, and that sufficient funds be provided from the cooperative program of the North Carolina Baptist Convention to care for the needs and expansion of this school year by year where necessary and possible.[16]

Dr. Perry Crouch, executive secretary of the North Carolina Baptist State Convention, requested that a way be found for the establishment of satellite centers of the Department of Pastoral Care across the state. In April 1974, the first satellite center was established as the Fayetteville Family Life Center, Inc., with its first director being Dr. James A. Hyde. Dr. Ted Dougherty was responsible for opening this center. The goals were to establish ministries of education, counseling, and enrichment within the regional area of North Carolina. The training provided was accredited by the Association for Clinical Pastoral Education, Inc., and those counseling were certified by the American Association of Pastoral Counselors and/or the American Association of Marriage and Family Therapists. The current director at Fayetteville is Dr. John Mackey.

In five years satellite centers were also established in three other cities in North Carolina. In June 1975, Dr. Ted Dougherty was also responsible for opening the Life Enrichment Center in Raleigh. The Rev. Charles Wilson, by now a full-time pastoral counselor in the Pastoral Counseling Division, was responsible for the beginning of the Western North Carolina Life Enrichment Center, Inc., in Morganton in February of 1976. The first director of this center was the Rev. George Carter. Dr. Dwight Cumbee was director at Raleigh, and Dr. J. John Edgerton, III, presently serves at Morganton. The Rev. Howard Doerle was added to the staff at Morganton in 1981. The Raleigh center became independent of the Department of Pastoral Care in January 1986.

The Baptist Hospital's Community Counseling Center (formerly known as the Baptist Counseling Center) in Charlotte was begun in July 1976, under the direction of the Rev. Craig Weaver. This center is presently directed by Dr. Thomas H. O'Neal.

Other staff and associate staff persons in the system who have served, or are now serving, are: Ethel Ethington, Everett Thomas, Kit Schooley, Alan Hanson, Van Brown, Lyman Ferrell, Charles Van Wagner, Skip Mericle, Ann McLaughlin, Dana Jenkins Kilby, Steve Duncan, Ron Erickson, Miriam Anne Glover, and Diane Moore Boyles

With such an expansion of the services reaching out to several areas of the state, it became important to re-evaluate goals and purposes The Statement of Mission of the staff and faculty of the Department of Pastoral Care reads:

> Believing in God
>> Whose grace we experience in Jesus Christ,
>>> and responding to persons who need
>>>> hope in the midst of despair,
>>>>> wholeness in the midst of brokenness,
> We declare our Mission of Pastoral Care to be . . .
>> service and education for ministry through
>>> clinical pastoral education,
>>>> hospital ministry,
>>>>> pastoral counseling,
>>>>>> leadership development, and
>>>>>>> life enrichment.
>>>>>>>> Shalom!

The School of Pastoral Care Foundation, Inc., was incorporated in August 1974 to aid the Department of Pastoral Care in continuing its expanding ministries. The initial board of directors and officers elected were: Mr. Leon Rice, Jr., chairman; Dr. Eugene B. Linton, vice chairman; the Rev. Wesley E. Brett, secretary and treasurer; the Rev. J. Dewey Hobbs, Jr., the Rev. Calvin S. Knight, and Dr. Andrew D. Lester. The purpose of the Foundation was to provide monetary aid and support to the programs and personnel of the Department of Pastoral Care, to provide grants and other support to worthy individuals for the purpose of attending the programs and services of the department, to provide support to the department. . . . Christian ministries of counseling, consultation, education, and enrichment, to support and encourage the expansion of such ministries, and finally, to operate for religious and educational purposes for the support and encouragement of pastoral care and counseling.

In 1974 extended units of CPE were added to the training programs. In light of the time crunch of many pastors, the school pioneered the use of a two-days per week program for an extended period of time. This enabled pastors to participate in basic units of Clinical Pastoral Education.

A memorial fund in memory of Dr. Richard K. Young was established soon after his death in 1975. This fund is used to provide financial aid to students and supports the school's library.

Mr. Marshall Kurfees was honored at the 19th Alumni Institute. He had served as director of the Committee for a Model Community program at the School of Pastoral Care for fourteen years. He was responsible for channeling nearly a quarter of a million dollars into the school from various community resources. He has played a significant part in the growth, development, and outreach of the Department of Pastoral Care.

In 1974 the Division of Pastoral Counseling instituted a fee system. The primary purpose for beginning to charge fees for counseling was the therapeutic benefit to counselees in taking responsibility for their counseling. The fees were also quite helpful in allowing for the coverage and expenses of the expansion of counseling programs. The fee system was on a sliding scale, and helped the satellite centers to grow and maintain vital services throughout the state.

The Division of Human Enrichment and Development established in 1973 grew rapidly. Programs of this division used small groups for facilitating growth for change in persons, families, and institutions throughout the state. Growth and enrichment experiences were expressed primarily through what was known as Shalom Events. There were 30 short-term events held in the state during 1974 with a total number of participants being 503. These events are offered in three major areas: personal growth retreats and seminars, family enrichment retreats and seminars, and institutional retreats and seminars. Other events included bereavement, recovery, seminars on women's issues, and human relations workshops for management. Presently, the Shalom events are under the direction of Mr. Neil Chafin who also directs the work of the School of Pastoral Care Foundation.

There were several significant personnel changes in 1976. Dr. Andrew D. Lester, who had directed the department for five years, resigned to assume duties as professor of pastoral care at Southern Baptist Theological Seminary. Dr. M. Mahan Siler, who was the first director of the Division of Human Enrichment and Development, was appointed the new director, and Dr. Ted Dougherty was named as director of the Division of Pastoral Counseling.

A most significant event occurred at this time when the pastoral counseling training program was accredited as a training center by the American Association of Pastoral Counselors. At that time only five training programs in the nation had received accreditation.

New facilities strengthened the work of the department. With the construction of Watlington Hall, the department was able to provide new quarters for staff and students in the Division of Clinical Pastoral Education. This new facility enabled administrative offices and pastoral counseling to move to buildings on the corner of Queen and Hawthorne. In 1979 the Pastoral Care Library was centralized on the ground floor adjacent to the student quarters in the chapel basement. The library has been in existence since the early days when classes began. Mrs. Elizabeth Averitt has been part-time librarian since the early 1970s.

Additional chaplaincy services were provided through the closed circuit television to patients' rooms. The Olivia Hall Fund made it possible to have worship services, as well as other religious programs, taped for viewing by patients in their rooms.

The staff increases reflect the expansion of services offered by the medical center. In the Division of Clinical Pastoral Education, which is also responsible for chaplaincy services to patients, families, and medical personnel, employment of additional staff members sought to keep pace with the growth of the hospital. The Rev. H. Mac Wallace joined the staff in 1979 as a chaplain supervisor, and the Rev. S. Bryant Kendrick, Jr. assumed the position as chaplain to students. Through continuing education both of these men recently obtained their Doctor of Ministry degrees from Southeastern Baptist Theological Seminary. In the Division of Pastoral Counseling, the Rev. Charles Wilson, who had been for a number of years chaplain to students in the medical center, became a full-time pastoral counselor. In 1982 the counseling division staff increased with the employment of the Rev. Meredith Neill, as associate staff member, and Dr. Daniel Jungkuntz.

Dr. Swan Haworth relinquished his post as the director of the Division of Pastoral Counseling in 1978, but remained on the staff as senior counseling consultant and supervisor. Dr. Haworth was a pioneer in pastoral counseling. He began developing his skills as early as 1928 while serving as a pastor in rural Kentucky. In the early thirties opportunities for specialized help were limited. However, he attended psychiatric conferences and read broadly in the field of human behavior. While director of the counseling division, he developed relationships with Mandala Center, a psychiatric hospital. Here he supervised the work of pastoral counseling students and functioned as a member of the therapeutic team. He continued to serve until his retirement in January 1986, for health reasons, at which time the title of pastoral counselor emeritus was bestowed upon him. He was able to make a tremendous contribution to the field of pastoral care through his ministry in the Department of Pastoral Care. His influence on students, as well as counselees, will be passed on to other generations of pastoral counselors and others whose lives he has touched and whose burdens he has lightened.

Dr. David R. Mace, internationally known for his work involving marriage and the family, joined the staff in 1976. Dr. Mace directed marriage enrichment training in the Division of Human Enrichment and Development and continued to serve as professor in the Department of Family Sociology with the Bowman Gray School of Medicine. He functioned in this capacity until his retirement several years ago.

Under the directorship of Dr. Siler the department sought to consolidate its continued growth and expansion. Siler gave attention to the culture of the system, which had now grown to be the largest of its kind in the world. He assisted the department in reviewing goals and values. He was especially committed to maintaining a supportive cohesiveness within the staff in the midst of tensions created with growth and change. Dr. Siler resigned as director in June of 1983 to assume the pastorate of the Pullen Memorial Baptist Church in Raleigh, North Carolina.

Dr. J. Dewey Hobbs, Jr., who had been pastor of the First Baptist Church in Marion, North Carolina, for twenty years, a denominational leader and a faithful supporter of the department's ministry, was appointed director in 1984 and continues to serve in that position.

Services and educational opportunities continue to increase. The department is reporting the largest number of hospital ministries in its existence. Support groups for patients, families, and medical staff became a major emphasis about five years ago. Records indicate that during this time 2,707 were in operation. Additionally, during this period there were 1,384 worship services in the medical center, and 9,548 on-call ministries.

Enrollment continues to be high in the various CPE and pastoral counseling programs. An extended unit of Clinical Pastoral Education was conducted for chaplains at the Veterans Administration Hospital in Salisbury under the direction of the Rev. Robert C. Spilman in 1985. Another extended unit was conducted in Asheville under the supervision of the Rev. Ron Erickson. A one-year contract was entered into in 1986 with the Hickory Memorial Psychiatric Hospital to provide clinical pastoral education to area ministers. This program is being developed and supervised by Dr. John Edgerton of the Morganton center. Pastoral counseling services are presently offered, as an extension of the Morganton center, in North Wilkesboro by the Rev. Steve Duncan. Also, Dr. John Mackey of the Fayetteville center provides counseling in Rockingham one day a week.

The enrichment programs, started under the HED Division, continue under the auspices of the School of Pastoral Care Foundation, Inc. Recently, special seminars have been provided for pastors in transition. The Shalom Events continue to involve a number of persons around the state for seminars and workshops on journal writing, marriage enrichment, Myers-Briggs testing and leadership training, among others.

The Ministers Care Plan was a significant breakthrough in responding to the needs of ministers and their dependents. The School of Pastoral Care Foundation, Inc., has contracts with three denominations to administer funds to subsidize counseling for ministers and their families: N.C. Baptist, Moravian, and United Church of Christ. In addition, the Western North Carolina Conference of the United Methodist Church provides assistance to their ministers and works through their program on an individual basis.

Since its inception, the chaplain to students program has shared the support of both the hospital and medical school. In the immediate future, this program will be supported entirely by the Bowman Gray School of Medicine. Dr. Kendrick has been employed to serve on the faculty of the medical school full-time as of July 1, 1987, to teach medical ethics.

The department has sought to be an extension of the good news of love and grace proclaimed by the Church. It has sought to be the love of God as well as proclaim it. Not only has this been of tremendous value and an outstanding contribution to the healing ministry of the medical center, it has had an outreach of service in the community, the state, nation, and around the world. The Department of Pastoral Care has been referred to as the "soul" of the medical center, making explicit through service and outreach the actualizations of the purpose of this medical center.

References and Notes

1. Anton T. Boisen, *Exploration of the Inner World.* New York: Willett Clark and Company, 1936.
2. Meredith W. Neill, *The Contribution of Richard K. Young to Pastoral Care Among Southern Baptists.* Unpublished Th.M. thesis, Southeastern Baptist Theological Seminary, 1983, pp. 12–13.
3. Richard K. Young, "The Southern Baptist Hospital Chaplaincy." (Th.D. dissertation, Southern Baptist Theological Seminary, 1951), p. 22.
4. Personal interview by L.L. McGee with Joe Fred Luck, 1962.
5. Minutes of the meeting of Trustees of the North Carolina Baptist Hospital, January 1953.
6. Meredith W. Neill, *op.cit.*
7. Chapel address given by Egbert L. Davis, Jr., 1954.
8. Department of Pastoral Care Annual Report to Trustees of North Carolina Baptist Hospitals, Inc., for the year 1960.
9. Minutes of meeting of Trustees, October 26, 1961.
10. A personal interview by Carolyn B. Harrell, Senior Secretary in the Department of Pastoral Care, with Mr. Marshall C. Kurfees, April 23, 1987.
11. Winston-Salem Journal, "Young Receiving Psychiatric Treatment," 23 October 1962, p. 20.
12. Twin City Sentinel, "A Letter From Dr. Young," 8 December 1962, p. 2.

13. Wayne E. Oates, "Memorial Meditation for Richard K. Young," meditation given at Davis Memorial Chapel, North Carolina Baptist Hospital, 18 March 1975.
14. Minutes of meeting of Trustees of North Carolina Baptist Hospital, October 2, 1972.
15. *Ibid.*
16. *Ibid.*

Statement to the Faculty Executive
Council by the Executive Dean
December 21, 1960
Graylyn Retreat
PROBLEMS OF THE NEXT FIVE YEARS

The problems that the medical school will face during the next five years depend on the kind of school we wish to develop. If our only purposes are to produce reasonably competent practitioners prepared for current medical practice, and to supply good medical care for western North Carolina, the solutions for our problems are simple. Hospital and professional domination is desirable, a quasi relationship with Wake Forest College is satisfactory, conflicts between academic and organized medicine will dissolve, and the cost of operating the medical school will greatly diminish. On the other hand, if we wish to produce competent physicians who are students of medicine, if we wish to train teacher-investigators, if we wish to make significant contributions through research, and if we wish to take a position of responsible leadership in medical care, our problems are legion. Their solution will require wisdom and aggressive action by the administration and the entire faculty.

I am assuming that we all take this last point of view. If not, this is our major problem, and it needs to be resolved immediately. The question should be the first item on the agenda during our discussion period. In taking this point of view, the medical school must face in two directions. One face points to the university which must orient our academic programs and administrative policies. The other points to the community and the medical profession. This is a difficult posture to maintain, and the cause of a number of our problems. I believe that a medical school must develop two legitimate faces. If it ignores university ties and tradition, it will lose primary concern for education and scholarship. If it ignores the community and the profession, it can easily lose perspective and public support, and fail to exert its full influence on improving the quality of medical care. A number of medical educators would disagree with this opinion and urge total orientation to the university.

In the following brief discussion, I have limited myself to four problem areas, because I know that others related more specifically to departments and the hospital will be brought up in the individual reports that follow.

1. *Financing.* Future financing will be dependent to a large extent on designated funds from the federal government and our medical service plan. The maintenance of institutional control over the growth and balance of activities and the assurance of an equitable distribution of financial support will continue to be a major problem. Our greatest need is to increase *unrestricted* institutional funds. Through the enforcement of sound policies of financing based on program cost analysis and the careful use of the new institutional research grant from the National Institutes of Health, some basic dollar can be freed for the support of medical education and other basic activities of the school. We must continue to seek, at a high priority, more endowed professorships and unrestricted gifts and grants. Tuition must be increased in a step-wise fashion to $1,200 per year as soon as adequate student loan funds are available.

2. *Faculty.* An analysis of faculty losses during the past five years and the number of budgeted unfilled positions that have existed during this year indicate that our problem has been one of faculty procurement rather than maintenance. The procurement of well qualified faculty will become increasingly difficult as the "holding effect" of the NIH research fellowship and professorship programs becomes evident and as new medical schools develop. In most instances we are highly competitive with regard to total faculty income and fringe benefits. The lack of a strong graduate program has been the major deterrent to the recruitment of faculty in the basic medical sciences. The lack of a Ph.D. program appears to be a major cause also for our relatively poor record in obtaining good fellowship candidates in these fields.

We have few positions on the clinical faculty that are competitive with regard to time for academic activities. The amount of effort now required in fee-for-service activities is not attractive to younger men and has limited the academic potential of the existing faculty. Some way must be developed to reduce non-academic demands on the individual faculty member without jeopardizing patient care. This will require additions to the clinical faculty and financial support.

It is my conviction that more effort and money must be spent on "growing our own" faculty through the development of Ph.D. programs and through the encouragement and financial support of promising medical students, house officers, and clinical trainees who show an interest in an academic career. The stigmata of inbreeding can be avoided if the plan for academic training is thoughtfully designed to include experiences in other institutions. Early post-doctoral support is available for promising candidates in the basic medical sciences. Similar support is not available for the clinical disciplines. I suggest that the medical school and the Medical Foundation sponsor jointly one or more teaching fellowships in each clinical discipline which will adequately support promising young men until they are eligible for fellowships sponsored by agencies or foundations. A valuable byproduct of a teaching fellow program will be closer supervision and more tutorial instruction for students during their clerkships which is an urgent need in all departments.

3. *Medical education.* Inadequacies in our curriculum and methods of teaching have been brought into focus through faculty discussions, the work of the Committee on Medical Education, the Liaison Committee, and the National Boards. Our Committee believes that teaching can be greatly improved by strengthening the faculty; by a comprehensive re-appraisal of objectives, course content and teaching methods; and through the correction of defects in the structure of the present curriculum. You are aware of the problems which will attend necessary changes. We must face these during the coming year. I believe we are reaching the point where a person is needed who will spend half time on research in medical education. I feel this is necessary if we are to evaluate our teaching properly and give continuing emphasis to the primary educational responsibility of the faculty.

4. *Public Relations with the Medical Profession.* This is a problem that primarily concerns the full-time clinical faculty. During the past two years, we have had two skirmishes with segments of the local profession—directly through the debate on the Medical Center concept and indirectly through the Cayer-Sohmer-McMillan issue. Both issues are still active, and can materially affect our future. We cannot ignore the impact of the new Forsyth General Hospital. Should we adopt the ivory tower position, or should we show a greater interest in

the medical profession and in the improvement of medical care in the community? My personal opinion has been stated earlier. I do not know the proper tactical approaches to this problem, but feel this area is worthy of immediate attention.

M. Meads; December 21, 1960

Administration of the Medical Center
1941-1983

Wake Forest College/Wake Forest University
  Thurman D. Kitchin
    President 1930-1950

  Harold W. Tribble
    President 1950-1967

  J. Ralph Scales
    President 1967-1983

  Thomas K. Hearn, Jr.
    President 1983 -

The Bowman Gray School of
Medicine of Wake Forest College/
University
  Coy C. Carpenter
    Dean 1936-1963

    Vice President for Health Affairs
    1963-1967

  Manson Meads
    Executive Dean 1959-1963

    Dean 1963-1971

    Vice President for Health Affairs
    1967-1983

    Director of the Medical Center
    1974-1983

North Carolina Baptist Hospital

  Smith Hagaman
    Superintendent 1934-1945

  Ray E. Brown
    Administrator 1943-1945

  Reid T. Holmes
    Administrator 1945-1970

    President 1970-1974

213

Richard Janeway
Dean 1971–

Vice President for Health
Affairs 1983–

Co-director of the Medical
Center 1983–

John E. Lynch
Executive Vice President
1970–1972

Chief Executive Officer 1972–

President 1974–

Co-director of the Medical
Center 1983–

Department Chairpersons
(1941–1983)

Anatomy

Herbert M. Vann, M.D.	1941–1946
Richard A. Groat, Ph.D.	1947–1952
Warren Andrew, M.D.	1952–1958
Norman M. Sulkin, Ph.D.	1958–1959 (Interim)
	1959–1975
Walter Bo, Ph.D.	1976 (Interim)
W. Keith O'Steen, Ph.D.	1977–

Anesthesia

Thomas H. Irving, M.D.	1969–1982
Francis M. James, III, M.D.	1983–

Biochemistry

Camillo Artom, M.D.	1941–1961
Cornelius F. Strittmatter, IV, Ph.D.	1961–1978
B. Moseley Waite, Ph.D.	1978–

Community Medicine

Donald M. Hayes, M.D.	1970–1976
James A. Chappell, M.D.	1976–1977 (Interim)

Comparative Medicine

Thomas B. Clarkson, D.V.M.   1972–

Dentistry

Charles R. Jerge, D.D.S.   1978–

Family and Community Medicine (Family Medicine 1974–1977)

Julian F. Keith, M.D.   1974–

Medical Social Science and Marital Health

Clark E. Vincent, Ph.D.   1975
Marvin B. Sussman, Ph.D.   1976–1978

Medicine

Tinsley R. Harrison, M.D.   1941–1944
George T. Harrell, Jr., M.D.   1944–1946 (Interim)
                                               1946–1952
Ernest H. Yount, Jr., M.D.   1952–1972
Joseph E. Johnson, III, M.D.   1972–

Microbiology and Immunology (Bacteriology 1941–1948)

Edward S. King, M.D.   1941–1946
McDonald Fulton, Ph.D.   1946–1948
Dorothy M. Tuttle, Ph.D.   1949   (Interim)
Parker R. Beamer, M.D.   1949–1953
Dorothy M. Tuttle, Ph.D.   1953–1954
Robert L. Tuttle, M.D.   1955–1963
Quentin N. Myrvik, Ph.D.   1963–1981
Charles E. McCall, M.D.   1981–   (Interim)

Neurology

Martin G. Netsky, M.D.	1960–1961
James F. Toole, M.D.	1962–1983
Richard Janeway, M.D.	1969–1970 (Interim)
B. Todd Troost, M.D.	1983–

Obstetrics and Gynecology

Frank R. Lock, M.D.	1941–1966
Richard L. Burt, M.D.	1966–1972
Frank C. Greiss, M.D.	1972–

Pathology

Coy C. Carpenter, M.D.	1941–1946
Robert P. Morehead, M.D.	1946–1973
Robert W. Prichard, M.D.	1973–

Pediatrics

Leroy J. Butler, M.D.	1941–1950
Robert B. Lawson, M.D.	1950–1954
Weston M. Kelsey, M.D.	1954–1973
Jimmy L. Simon, M.D.	1974–

Physiology and Pharmacology

Herbert S. Wells, Ph.D.	1941–1944
Harold D. Green, M.D.	1945–1963
J. Maxwell Little, Ph.D.	1963–1973 (Pharmacology only)
Harold D. Green, M.D.	1963–1972 (Physiology only)
N. Sheldon Skinner, M.D.	1972–1973 (Physiology only) 1973–1974
Alvin Brodish, Ph.D.	1975–

Preventive Medicine

George T. Harrell, Jr., M.D.	1943–1946
Thomas T. Mackie, M.D.	1946–1951
Manson Meads, M.D.	1951–1957
Lucile W. Hutaff, M.D.	1953–1955 (Interim)
C. Nash Herndon, M.D.	1957–1969

Psychiatry (Neuropsychiatry 1946–1953; Psychiatry and Neurology 1953–1978; Psychiatry and Behavioral Medicine 1979–)

Lloyd J. Thompson, M.D.	1953–1956
Angus C. Randolph, M.D.	1957–1959 (Interim)
Richard C. Proctor, M.D.	1960–

Radiology

James P. Rousseau, M.D.	1941–1949
J. Robert Andrews, M.D.	1950–1954
Isadore Meschan, M.D.	1955–1977
C. Douglas Maynard, M.D.	1977–

Surgery

Howard H. Bradshaw, M.D.	1941–1968
Richard T. Myers, M.D.	1968–

Board of Visitors*
(1959–1983)

Chairpersons

Bowman Gray	1959
James A. Gray, Jr.	1960–1961
Albert L. Butler, Jr.	1961–1969
John F. Watlington, Jr.	1969–1983
J. Paul Sticht	1983–

Members

Charles H. Babcock	1959–1960
Mrs. Winifred P. Babcock	1969–1973
Mrs. Vicki Bagley	1974–1979
Herbert Brenner	1981–
Albert L. Butler, Jr.	1959–
Irving E. Carlyle	1959–1969
William B. Cash	1969–
Richard Chatham	1974–1982
William J. Conrad	1959–1969
Thomas H. Davis	1972–
Mrs. Anne R. Forsyth	1959–1965

*The board was established in April 1959 as the successor to the orginal Advisory Council to the Dean of the Medical School. It extended its interest to include the North Carolina Baptist Hospital in 1962 and officially became the Medical Center Board of Visitors by joint Trustee approval in 1974.

James K. Glenn	1969–
Bowman Gray	1959–1966
Bowman Gray, III	1969–1970
Mrs. Elizabeth C. Gray	1971–1974
Gordon Gray	1963–1982
James A. Gray, Jr.	1959–1970
Lyons Gray	1974–
Mrs. Barbara L. Hanes	1970–
James G. Hanes	1959–1960
P. Huber Hanes, Jr.	1969–1974
Ralph P. Hanes	1961–1973
Petro Kulynych	1979–
William R. Lybrook	1961–1981
John G. Medlin, Jr.	1981–
Claude S. Ramsey, Jr.	1981–
Richard J. Reynolds, Jr.	1959–
Earl F. Slick	1981–
W. Roger Soles	1974–1982
J. Paul Sticht	1974–
Colin Stokes	1970–
John F. Watlington, Jr.	1963–

Presidents of the Medical Alumni Association

1943–1945	Louten R. Hedgpeth '31
1946	Bahnson Weathers '15
1947	G. Oren Moss '25
1948	Felda Hightower '31
1949–1950	Thomas W. Baker '29
1951–1952	D. Russell Perry, Sr. '17
1953	Ernest W. Furguson '34
1954	Eugene C. Clayton '45
1955	H. Fleming Fuller '34
1956	Vernon W. Taylor, Jr. '36
1957	L. Randolph Doffermyre '35
1958	Roscoe L. Wall, Sr. '10
1959	Claude A. McNeill '43
1960	D. E. Ward, Jr. '45
1961	George W. Paschal, Jr. '29
1962	D. Russell Perry, Jr. '46
1963	J. O. Williams, Jr. '46
1964	Hubert M. Poteat, Jr. '38
1965	Julian F. Keith '53
1966	W. Walton Kitchin '38
1967	W. Boyd Owen '40
1968	William H. Freeman '44
1969	Robert P. Crouch '54
1970	Joseph B. Alexander '47
1971	Claude A. McNeill '43
1972	Jefferson D. Beale '44
1973	John W. Nance '48
1974	Jean B. Brooks '44
1975	Ernest H. Stines '57

1976	Giles L. Cloninger '54
1977	Wayne A. Cline '46
1978	Livingston Johnson '51
1979	Robert C. Pope '45
1980	C. James Walton '55
1981	Murphy F. Townsend, Jr. '61
1982	Gary B. Copeland '60
1983	Dixie L. B. Soo '59

Index for Articles by Invited Contributors